(WATLINGS)

ESPAÑOLA
(HAITI, Dominican
Republic)

Navidad   Isabela

Santa
Domingo

San Juan   THE VIRGINS

SAN
JUAN

SANTA
CRUZ

MONTSERRATE
GUADALUPE
LOS SANTOS

DOMINICA

BARBADOS

ASUNCION

TRINIDAD

VENEZUELA

Columbus And The New World

COLUMBUS
And The New World

by AUGUST DERLETH
illustrated by Dirk Gringhuis

VISION BOOKS

Farrar, Straus and Cudahy   New York
Burns and Oates   London

VISION BOOKS

IS A DIVISION OF

FARRAR, STRAUS & CUDAHY, INC.

PUBLISHED SIMULTANEOUSLY IN CANADA BY
AMBASSADOR BOOKS, LTD., TORONTO
MANUFACTURED IN THE U. S. A.

Nihil Obstat:
Rt. Rev. Msgr. Peter B. O'Connor
Censor Librorum

Imprimatur:
✠ Most Reverend Thomas A. Boland, S.T.D.
Archbishop of Newark

Contents

Author's Note

The real name of Christopher Columbus has often been a subject of dispute. I have chosen in this book to use the name by which he is best known to English-speaking peoples, but evidence suggests that he was born Christoforo Colombo. He himself most often in his adult life signed his name "Christóbal Colón"; he was also known in his own time by the name of Christavao Colom or Colomo.

I have chosen also to retain the names of the lands discovered by Columbus as he set them down. On his first voyage Columbus landed at San Salvador or Watlings Island (which he called Guanahani), and explored the Bahama Islands, Santo Domingo (Española), and Cuba. On his second, he discovered the Lesser Antilles, Dominica, and Puerto Rico. On his third, Trinidad and the coast of South America, and on his fourth and last voyage, Columbus explored the coast of Honduras, Nicaragua, Costa Rica, and Panama, and spent a year on the island of Jamaica. During all this time, which encompassed more than twelve years, Columbus was convinced that he was among the islands known as the Indies and described by the traveler, Marco Polo, as belonging to the Grand Khan of Cathay (China). The principal island and chief object of Columbus' search was named Cipango (Japan).

In addition to the usual references, I was particularly helped in the writing of this book by three excellent books, than which I know of nothing in English more comprehensive or authoritative— *Christopher Columbus* by Salvador de Madariaga; *Admiral of the Ocean Sea* and *Christopher Columbus, Mariner*, by Samuel Eliot Morison. Any question, however, particularly in matters of names and their spellings, I resolved by recourse to de Madariaga.

1 *The Sinking of the* Bechalla

FROM one lookout to another among the ships
of the convoy that moved up along the coast of
Portugal one day in August, 1476, went the
shouted news that ships lay to seaward. Questions
flew across the blue water.

"Under what flag?"

"No flag, sir."

"Pirates?"

Below, the sailors listened. The convoy was

armed. Pirates would not dare attack. Besides, they were not far off Portugal, and pirates would not be apt to linger so close to the shore where the vessels of King John could fall upon them. The convoy had set out from home—Genoa, Italy— months before. It was now even farther from its goal in the north of Europe than it was from home.

A growing tension among the lookouts and the captains spread to the men who manned the ships of the convoy.

"What do you think, Christopher?" asked one of the sailors of another. Both men were from Genoa; they had known each other before signing as seamen for the voyage. "Would they be ships bound for Lisbon?"

"No, Guilio," answered Christopher. "If they were Portuguese ships, their flags would be flying."

Guilio Faracci shot an uneasy glance seaward. "They're pressing in!"

Christopher Columbus heard the captain's order to the ships to draw in toward shore. "Don't be alarmed," he said. "Portugal is a great country for exploration. Ships from all countries come here."

But he had hardly spoken when an excited shouting passed from one ship to another.

"French flags broken out!"

"Task force! Prepare for battle!"

At once everyone on the ships of the convoy was flung into a bustle of activity. Orders were shouted, men ran to and fro in obedience, the armed convoys moved out to do battle, and the merchant ships tried to arrange themselves behind the convoying vessels.

The French attackers, aided by a strong wind, moved in swiftly and began to fire at the Genoese ships before they were ready to reply with their own guns.

Soon all was indescribable confusion. Cannon balls struck and burst in the wooden vessels. Fires broke out and were quenched. Shouted orders went unheard in the noise of battle. The roar of cannons and the barking of small arms, the cata- pulting of firebrands, the thickening smoke—all added to the chaos aboard the ships of the convoy.

The *Bechalla*, on board which were Guilio and Columbus, was one of the forward ships. There was no time for talk now between the two young men. Indeed, they seldom had even a glimpse of each other. They were so busy watching for the torches from the attacking ships and putting out the fires they started that they lost all track of time.

Columbus tried again and again to count the attacking ships, but he could not. Smoke, the turmoil of battle, and the movements of the ships made it impossible. But it seemed to him that the forces were well matched. He was not as excited or alarmed as many of his fellow sailors until a priest walked by along the deck, praying in a loud, firm voice, to remind Columbus and all the others that death went among them.

He saw a ship go down—one of the Genoese. It was not far away. Through a rift in the smoke soon after, he saw one of the French vessels listing badly in the water. He began to wonder how many others had been lost. Whenever he could, he looked among the ships which had set out from Genoa. Two were unaccounted for.

The battle raged, hour after hour. It had begun in the morning. Noon passed at the height of battle, and the sun began to move closer to the western rim. Still the battle went on. If two of the Genoese ships were lost, there were certainly as many of the attackers gone, too, Columbus was sure. Their numbers no longer seemed so great. But the battle was just as violent.

Suddenly—Columbus did not know how it

came about—the *Bechalla* lay in the direct line of
fire. No armed ship was there to protect her from
the cannons of the French. In a flash, danger
loomed before Columbus. He murmured a prayer
and commended his soul to God. Scarcely a moment later he felt a ball pierce his breast—too high,
he thought, to be mortal. Within a short time
thereafter, the ship shuddered under the full im-
pact of the cannon fire which was directed at it.

Then the *Bechalla* seemed to come apart. It
broke in two, and at the same time it began rapidly
to sink. Men were leaping or being thrown into the
sea on all sides of Columbus. He himself was swept
off his feet. He felt himself falling. In another moment, he felt the cold water close over him.

He came bobbing up. The cannons' roar still
went on. Cries for help rose all around him, but
now the other ships seemed too far to come in
time. A spar came floating past. Despite the pain
of his wound, Columbus grabbed at it, missed,
grabbed again, making a desperate lunge. He clung
grimly to the spar.

When he had recovered from his alarm and excitement a little, Columbus looked around him.
No sign of Guilio. He saw one sailor go down and

come up no more. Then another. The ships were too busy to help the drowning. Even now, the swirling battle was carrying them away from the grave of the *Bechalla*. And, at the same time, the sun dipped under the horizon, and the dusk began to settle over the sea.

Columbus rested on his spar.

The billows bore him away from the scene of the battle. He could still hear the rattle of musketry and the boom of the cannon. The sea behind him glowed red from the flames of burning ships looming out of the twilight. It seemed to him that all life separated him from the convoy of which he had been so much a part for all these weeks past.

Life—and perhaps death. He could not tell how much blood he had lost from his wound. He felt weak but not exhausted. The waves lulled him even while the water chilled him each time a wave broke over him. He did not know how far away the coast was, but there was no help to be hoped for from the ships behind him. And now, with darkness coming upon the ocean, he would soon be lost indeed.

But no—not quite lost. God watched over him. Even as he began a prayer for succor, he felt a pang of conscience. How he had wasted his twenty-four years! And was he not now wasting his twenty-fifth—perhaps his last? When his father had named him Christopher—after that St. Christopher who bore the Christ Child on his back —he had not intended that his son be only a wool-weaver like his parents. Nor a seaman, either— though the boy had shown his love for the sea when he was only a freckle-faced lad with red hair, blue eyes, and a ruddy complexion such as he still had.

Perhaps he would die here in the sea he had loved, thought Columbus. When he was but ten years old, he had gone to Corsica to load dried fish. After that he had voyaged several times in the Mediterranean. He was not yet twenty when he had taken service with the king of Anjou as a sailor in a fleet of warships to battle the king of Aragon. The sea had been his life—that same sea that might now be his death.

He shivered with the cold. Still clinging to the spar, he began to kick his legs, pushing himself and the spar forward toward land. The billows, too, moved in this direction, and Columbus hoped he had not judged badly.

He was now alone in all the vast sea. He thought he still heard the rumble of the cannon. He could not be sure. The waves washed against him, making their own talk. Overhead, the first stars began to show. He knew them all. He thought of them as the lights of heaven. His prayers warmed him, and he felt less alone.

He did not know how long he could battle the waves and the cold. With God's help, perhaps he could be saved—saved to serve God more faithfully in his coming years, and to do more honor to his parents. Here, with the specter of death at his elbow, his life passed before his mind's eye—the dark loom at which he had worked in the little house in Genoa; old Dominic, his patient father, and his even more patient mother, Susanna. He heard her voice again, as he had heard it on the eve of his first sea voyage, when she had come upon him poring over a map.

"Is it only to be a sailor that you have studied such maps, Christopher?" she asked.

"I love the sea, Mama," he answered.

Her troubled eyes dwelt on him. "A sailor's life is a rough one—often a short one. You know the maps so well, Christopher. I had hoped you would look farther."

He had felt that somehow he betrayed his mother's hope by going to sea, but she had never afterward made any complaint. Yet now, faced with an end to his life, he knew indeed that he had wasted his years. He had gone from helping at the looms to roistering in the public house in Savona, and on to loafing on the sea—yes, even to piracy, for that was what his service with the king of Anjou amounted to! Small wonder he had not been pleasing to the eye of God when he had not even brought much happiness to his parents!

He resolved that if this were not to be the end of his mortal life, it would certainly be the end of his former way of life. He would begin once more. With God's help, he would learn to serve Him and, at the same time, make his mark in the world before God called him.

Strengthened by his resolve, Columbus swam harder than before. The sea was now black all around him. No light shone—only the light of the stars. They shone down like old friends—Polaris, the North Star; the Great Bear; Arcturus, the Spring-Bringer—all stars he had known since his boyhood. And he knew their positions so well that he used them as a guide to direct his course toward shore.

He pushed forward, filled with confidence. He no longer doubted that he was going in the right direction. If only his strength held out! If only God might see fit to grant him a little favor! He swam until he was too tired to swim farther. Then he clung to the spar and let the sea have its way with him until he had rested enough to swim again.

In this way he moved toward shore, which he knew was six miles from the scene of the battle, for only an hour before that meeting with the French ships, the pilot of the *Bechalla* had set their position. He swam and rested and swam again. Without the spar to rest on, he would have been lost indeed. None other had been saved. How strange it was! Whose hand had it been that put the spar in his path? Columbus did not doubt that it was the hand of God. And by the same token, he was sure that God had further plans for him.

He doubled his efforts. But now his wound throbbed with pain, and his tired muscles hurt with weariness. He had lost all track of time, though the movement of the stars in their places as the earth turned told him that hours had passed.

Now, as he looked earnestly ahead of him, he thought he could see from time to time a patch of deeper dark which rose out of the darkness. This might be land, he told himself. Whenever the waves permitted, he looked eagerly ahead. There was surely something to be seen, but Columbus did not know whether it was an island or the mainland of Portugal.

He rested for longer and longer periods. He was close to exhaustion, and he knew it was possible, even here, within sight of land, to slip off the spar and into the deep from which he would not rise again. He prayed anew, and, despite the mounting pain of his wound, he clung hard to the spar.

Land loomed ahead—not just the high rock he had first seen, but a long line, at first low in the water, but now growing, stretching as far as eye could see. It seemed to the weary Columbus that he moved toward it at a snail's pace. He was convinced that for every foot he pushed forward, the sea pulled him back another.

But at last his feet touched the pebbled bottom. The land lay just ahead. A great rock jutted forth into the sky. The early summer dawn was already lighting the east. Not far away stood a village.

Columbus let go the spar. The ocean swept away the wood which had borne him. He stumbled forward on his feet, wading through the shallow water. He tottered out on the pebbled beach. There he fell upon his knees and humbly thanked God, promising hereafter to serve Him better than he had done before.

Then he slid forward, only half conscious, and slept.

As the dawn brightened, a little group of fishermen found him lying there. They stood in a half circle around him. He seemed to be sleeping. Because he was lying on his face, they did not see his wound. They talked in low voices about what to do. At last they decided to awaken him.

Columbus started awake at their touch. He looked at the men in bewilderment and pulled himself up to a sitting position while the events of the past day and night came slowly back to him.

"See there!" cried one of the men, pointing excitedly. "He's wounded!"

Half a dozen arms were immediately extended to help Columbus to his feet.

He rose unsteadily.

"Tell me, please—where am I?" he asked.

Three or four of the men told him he had landed

at the village of Lagos. Columbus tried to think. How far could he be from Lisbon? Up the coast a way. Surely not far.

He was grateful for the support of their arms. He doubted that he could stand alone. They waited patiently for him to speak. He had learned enough Portuguese in his travels and studies to talk their language well enough so that they could understand him.

He told them his name and added, "I've got a brother—my younger brother, Bartholomew—in Lisbon. If I could get there . . ." Of the convoy he no longer thought; they had given him up for dead. Perhaps none of those ships had lasted out the battle.

The fishermen assured him that boats traveled often between Lagos and Lisbon. One of them pointed to the Rock of Sagres looming upon the sky and told Columbus that Prince Henry, the Navigator, had kept his sea rovers perched on top of it to watch the sea for many years and so protect Lisbon and its trade.

But Columbus could not travel now. He was too weak. He could barely stand without swaying. He had lost more blood from his wound than he had suspected, and his trial by water had worn him out.

He did not need to speak of his plight. It was so plain to see that one of the older fishermen pressed forward kindly and said, "Sir, there's room at my house. You could stay there until you're well enough to go to Lisbon."

Gratefully Columbus allowed the men to lead him from the beach into the village. There he was made comfortable, and a doctor was called to attend his wound.

It was from the doctor that he learned he would need to lie quiet not for days, but for weeks, before he could go on to look for his brother.

2   *Columbus Studies and Dreams*

On a day in September, Columbus found himself in the capital of Portugal. Lisbon was a beautiful city built on the hills which sloped to the Bay of Tagus on the edge of the Atlantic. It was a city of busy, well-paved streets, where Columbus was lost among the horses of knights and travelers, the ox carts of the peasants, the sedan chairs of the wealthy. The salty air of the sea lay among its houses, some of which were as much as four stories high, built of yellow stone and brick. From the dark doorways Columbus passed came the smells of tallow, musk, cinnamon and wine.

He found Bartholomew at the bookshop where his younger brother worked.

Bartholomew was overjoyed to see him. He had been lonely for his brothers—Christopher, Diego, Antonio—and now here was Christopher like a gift from heaven.

"But how will you get back to Genoa?" he asked, when Columbus had related his misfortune.

"I'm not going back."

"What will you do, then?"

"I'll find work. I want to study—to learn more. I had less schooling than you, Bartholomew—and none of us had too much."

Bartholomew took him to the old bookseller who was his employer. He explained that Christopher was his brother, and that, like him, he could read well, especially in Latin. He told him that Christopher knew Spanish, Italian, and Portuguese, and that he could also draw maps and sea charts, and was skilled in books and the study of astronomy.

The old man nodded, satisfied, and said there

was always room in the shop for another helper.

Columbus tried earnestly to settle down. The bookshop fascinated him. He loved the astrolabes, the sand clocks, and, most of all, the books. He took time whenever he could to pore over the maps and charts. He read more books than ever before.

He read particularly, again and again, in a copy of the manuscript left by Messer Marco Polo, the Venetian traveler who had reached the country of the Indies and the land of the Grand Khan far to the east. He read of these lands so much that they were always in his mind, and he turned over and over in his thoughts the strange names of those faraway lands—Cipango, the greatest of the 7,444 islands said to be in the sea of China off the coast of the Grand Khan's country. He loved the sound of the strange names Messer Marco Polo had set down—Ziamba and Java, Kondur, Pentan, and Samara, Sondur and Fanfur—and scores of others. And he thought that this wonderfully rich country must be a place above all else on earth to see.

It was part of the business of the bookshop to make charts, and Columbus spent some of his time at this occupation. He soon found that, however well books sold, charts were even more in demand.

Soon he began to talk to Bartholomew to convince him that the two of them should go into the business of making charts by themselves.

One day Bartholomew agreed.

Now, in addition to his studies of Latin and geography and everything else he wished to learn, Columbus had to find out about every new discovery so that the maps of the brothers Columbus would be the best ones to be had. So, each time a ship came into port from Africa or the Western Islands, Christopher or Bartholomew—sometimes both of them—went down to invite the pilot or the master to take a meal with them. Christopher would ply him with questions. Had the master seen anything new on his journey? A new river— a mountain range—a harbor? Perhaps even new lands? What lay beyond the Guinea coast? What was west of the Azores if not, surely, Cathay— the land of the Grand Khan?

West of the Azores no one had sailed for decades. And most of those who had done so had never returned or had come back reporting only sea and more sea. These questions no one could answer, though Columbus learned many new things, and soon the maps and charts prepared by the Columbus brothers were in great demand.

Each such inquiry only whetted Columbus' appetite the more. And each gave new impulse to his curiosity. At the same time, Columbus was filled with a growing restlessness. The need to know more was not satisfied with such casual inquiries as the brothers made of returning seamen. More and more often, Columbus denied the urge to take to the sea again himself, until at last, that autumn, he took service under the flag of Portugal. He set sail for Ireland and Iceland, which was also called Thule and thought to be the end of the land area of the earth.

He had many adventures, but there was one among them that he did not forget. It happened when his ship stopped at Galway, Ireland. There Columbus saw two dead people in a drifting boat. They were people of a kind he had never seen before—strange people. He tried to explain to his brother on his return.

"They had different eyes. It seemed to me they were slanted. Their faces were broad—and sort of flat. Their skins like leather. . . ."

"Of course, that could have been exposure to the sun in the boat—that would make the skin leathery and brown," Bartholomew said.

Christopher agreed. "Just the same—they were

dressed in a fashion I never saw before. And where did they come from? Some said from far in the north, but when I got to Iceland I saw none like them. They say there's nothing beyond Iceland but snow and ice—so they must have come from the west."

"But there's only sea to the west!"

"Somewhere lies Cathay, Bartholomew—Messer Marco Polo says . . ."

"Ah, but he went east—not west. And who knows? A dreamer's tales!"

Christopher shook his head. "There must be a sea route to Cathay."

Bartholomew waved him away. "Idle dreams! Those people you saw were surely from some northern tribe. Perhaps they left their ship or were taken out to sea and died of exposure."

Columbus said no more, but the memory of the two dead people haunted him. He began to seek out seamen who had sailed in the western area. Had they ever seen the like of the people he had seen in Galway? For months he asked in vain. Then one day an old seaman told him that two people with wide faces, who looked far different from Christian people, had been given up by the sea at the Island of Flowers in the Azores. Columbus was renewed in his belief.

On another day, he sat down to talk with the pilot of the king of Portugal. He told him of what he had seen in Galway—of the man and the once-beautiful woman the Irish held were from Cathay —but the pilot had never seen their like.

"One day, though," the pilot added, "when we were sailing about 450 leagues west of Cape St. Vincent, we caught sight of an odd piece of wood. We picked it up. It was carved differently—not by iron tools—but by some other unknown to us. And the design was such as I never saw before."

"Where could it have come from?" asked Columbus.

"Where but from the west?"

Whenever he chanced upon any bit of strange information, it seemed to Columbus to point to the unknown west. Though he worked diligently at his trade of mapmaking, with occasional time out for sea journeys, he did not neglect to read every report, every journal of a voyage, every log-book and every travel account upon which he could lay his hands. But always he returned to Marco Polo's account to read it over and to under-

line sentences and memorize passages until it
seemed that no one in all Lisbon could know what
Marco Polo had written so well as he.

This was not all he did. As he began to wonder
more and more about the mystery of the unknown
western sea, he looked to God for guidance, for he
felt stirring within him a purpose not yet formed,
and he remembered his promise to serve God if he
were saved from the sea. He went as often as he
could—sometimes every day—to the Convent of
the Saints to hear Mass and to pray.

This convent was the property of the Nuns of
the Military Order of St. James. It was used as a
home for the wives and daughters of crusaders.
Among these ladies who, like Columbus, attended
Mass, he saw one day a dark-eyed girl watching
him covertly.

Thereafter he found himself looking for her.
And always he met her eyes, for she, too, looked
for him. She began to creep into his thoughts.
When he pored over his books and maps, when he
drew his charts, even when he sat at table making
eager inquiries of sailors— Did people live on all
the earth? Were there men with tails? Were there
one-eyed people? Did the seas in the south boil as

the seas in the north froze?—he found himself thinking of her dark eyes watching him.

One day, when he could be patient no longer, he approached the sister superior of the convent, pointed out the young lady, and asked to be introduced to her.

"I will speak to her mother," answered the sister superior.

For a few days Columbus thought of nothing else but the young lady of the convent. Then, one morning after Mass, he was summoned to the presence of the sister superior.

Beside her stood his young lady!

Filipa Moniz Perestrello—that was her name. Her mother was a widow and her father had been —was this, too, God's sign—a sailor of renown and captain of Porto Santo, the island off the coast of Africa which was the foremost base of discovery in all Portugal.

They were not left alone together. One of the nuns sat as chaperon nearby while they talked, telling each other about themselves. She was shy. He was no less so.

When he took his leave of her, Columbus already looked forward to his next meeting with Filipa.

For many weeks Columbus paid court to her.

Then came the day when he made the formal request of Filipa's mother, begging that Filipa be permitted to become his wife.

After their marriage, they moved into the home of Dona Perestrello. Once again, the flame of Columbus' curiosity about what lay beyond the western sea burned bright. His mother-in-law encouraged his curiosity and put before him the instruments, charts and notes left by her husband.

These Columbus read with close attention. He studied his late father-in-law's logbooks. He compared the charts with those which had been made later by other navigators.

Filipa's brother was still governor of Porto Santo, and Columbus asked himself often if this was not the place to be if he wished to sail the western sea. There were many ships there, and it was one of the first ports touched upon by many who navigated along the Guinea coast and to the west.

He began to talk to Filipa, to persuade her to leave her mother's house and go with him to Porto Santo. Until this time Columbus had carried on his work with his brother. Maps and charts continued to be in great demand, for there was not another country on the face of the known earth which had more navigators eager to add new lands to the crown.

At the same time Columbus had not decreased his wide reading. He was as eager as ever to add to his knowledge of the world and its people. And he had studied, he was sure, every map or chart ever made of the western sea, hoping to find some key to the route to Cathay by way of the west. This Cathay of Marco Polo's was to the east by land, and Columbus was certain that it could be reached by water if one sailed into the west, since the earth was round.

Then, one evening over a cup of wine, Christopher learned from a sailor about yet another map. This man was also a master mariner in the king's service, such as Columbus had become through his many voyages since his coming to Portugal.

"Have you seen Toscanelli's map, Columbus?" he was asked.

Columbus shook his head.

The mariner explained that Toscanelli, a mathematician and physicist of Florence, Italy, had made

a map at the request of King John when the king
was still but a prince of Portugal in 1474. "I've
not seen it myself, Columbus, but they say Toscanelli wrote a long letter in which he set forth his
conclusions about the earth and the ways of sea
travel. In the map he's said to show how a journey
by sea towards the west should be begun, and what
places you should come to—where to sail, and
where to turn."

"Where is the map?" asked Columbus, excited
by hope.

The mariner shrugged. "Ah—I don't know. Put
away somewhere—perhaps in the king's library.
The king's advisers think little of it."

"I don't care what others may think. I must see
the map."

"Ah, that's easier said than accomplished, Columbus."

Early next day Columbus began his search. Toscanelli's map was known in most quarters where
he made inquiry, but none knew where it was. The
king had been disappointed in it. Yet, at the same
time, the king had granted the right to discover and
govern any lands on Toscanelli's map. So, who
knew? Perhaps Toscanelli knew better than the

king's navigators and astronomers. Perhaps, like Pierre d'Ailly, who had written in his book, *Imago Mundi*, that the distance between Africa and the eastern coast of Cathay could be sailed with the help of a good wind in but a few days, Toscanelli knew, or suspected, the routes to be taken so that this feat might be accomplished.

Little by little, Christopher learned more of Toscanelli's letter and map—that Toscanelli had made a mistake in measuring the circumference of the known land mass from Lisbon to the Indian coast; that he had guessed the distance across the sea to the west to be only 130°, which Columbus doubted; that he believed in a wealthy continent he called Antilia, which was halfway to Messer Marco Polo's Cathay. Yet none had ever seen Antilia, or its fabled Seven Cities, though others had written of it besides Toscanelli. The king's cosmographers did not believe in Antilia, or in Toscanelli, either.

The letter and map were indeed on a shelf in the king's library. Columbus worked diligently to see them. He knew the mapmakers for the king; he had worked for them himself. A word whispered here, a favor done there, and one day Columbus found himself reading Toscanelli's letter, and, afterwards, staring long at the map.

Both excited him immeasurably. True, there were mistakes in the letter, but no one could say the map was untrue. In the little time at his disposal Columbus made a rough copy of the map and committed to memory most of what Toscanelli had written.

Soon after, all was in readiness for the move to Porto Santo. It waited only on the birth of Columbus' first child—a son whom they called Diego.

Then the three of them moved to Porto Santo. The year was 1480.

3 Columbus Looks to the West

COLUMBUS did not change his way of life in Porto Santo. He continued to draw maps and charts. Now and then he went on voyages so that he might come to know everything there was to be known about winds, currents, and the far places where the ships touched. For a while he went to live in Funchal, Madeira, where he eagerly sought more knowledge of the Orient beyond the western sea.

But he grew ever more restless. Years had passed since he had been saved from death by sea. He had vowed to serve God, and, as yet, he had done nothing in His service. What was it he must do? He was sure God had given him signs. Perhaps he had not read them correctly?

One day, when he turned to his books, he came upon the prophecy of the Roman statesman and philosopher, Seneca, written in his *Medea*. Seneca had written: "There will come a time when the bonds of the seas will fall apart, and a great continent will be discovered. Then a pilot will reveal new worlds, and Thule will no longer be the end of the earth."

Christopher read and re-read this with mounting excitement. Was he not a pilot? And had he not traveled to Thule—for was not Iceland the last land, the land at the end of the earth? Then Seneca must have meant the Orient, the land called Cathay or China, and that other great island land named Cipango! And, if his prophecy was correct, then a pilot was destined by God to find that land.

On another day, while Columbus wandered along the waterfront at Funchal, he met an old man looking out to sea.

"Are you, too, waiting for ships to come in?" he asked jokingly.

"My shipping days are over," answered the old man. "I was once a navigator—but I tired of men who feared to go beyond the maps."

"In the Guinea trade?"

"Aye. I found only danger, and no daring. It turned sour on me." He guessed Columbus' interest and added, "Young man—we mariners are all agreed that the earth is round. We're all told that a voyage to Cathay could be made by sailing west. Why has no one ever done it? All fear the ocean and the places of the earth not yet on the maps, as if they've forgotten that someone must be the first to put them there, to mark the places for all the rest of the world to see."

Columbus' spirits leaped. He had thought this many times. He carried the old navigator's words with him for days, turning them over and over in his thoughts.

Then, late one night, when he was very tired after a day of hard work, Columbus took up his Bible and let it fall open. It parted at *Psalms,* and his eyes fell to the eighteenth psalm.

"The heavens show forth the glory of God, and

the firmament declareth the work of His hands.

"Day to day uttereth speech, and night to night sheweth knowledge.

"There are no speeches nor languages, where their voices are not heard.

"Their sound hath gone forth into all the earth: and their words unto the ends of the world . . ."

Columbus closed his eyes and fell to his knees. "The ends of the world . . ." All doubts, all the host of questions with which he had tormented himself throughout the years since he had landed at Lagos, vanished. His restlessness washed away. He knew what he must do. This opening of the Bible to these words was but a sign from God. It was God's will that he, Columbus, should be that pilot prophesied by Seneca to discover the lands beyond the end of the world and to bring to those who lived there the word of God.

He prayed long and fervently for God's help in his quest before he made his weary way to bed that night.

After that day, Columbus no longer had any doubt about the course he must follow. He was certain that he had read the signs from heaven correctly, that he was meant to seek the sea route to Cathay, and to bring God to those who lived at "the ends of the world." But he knew, too, that it would not be easy to reach this goal, for the king of Portugal was plagued by all manner of navigators who wanted to explore far lands. He could not grant them all help. Yet, without a commission from the king, Columbus could not hope to accomplish his mission.

He studied harder than ever. He read again not only Marco Polo and Cardinal d'Ailly, but also went back to original sources. He read Ptolemy and the Toledan tables. He made many notes. And the more he read and put down, the humbler he felt. "Is it not true," he wrote, "that every country has its own west and east in relation to its own horizon?" He marked differences between the books he read. "The tables of Alfonso done at Toledo put the Occident farther west than does Ptolemy," he noted. All his notes were bent toward the answer to a single question: which way to the Orient? How best to reach Cathay and Cipango?

Columbus spent many days in his study, making notes, checking one book against another. He referred again and again to Toscanelli's map, correcting what he thought were mistakes in that map, and making new maps of his own, for himself this time, and not to be sold to others. He was convinced, with Toscanelli, that if the distance by land between the edge of the west and the edge of the east were as long as all the authorities held it to be, then the distance between Spain and the Indies by sea was much smaller—perhaps even shorter than had ever been supposed.

At last, when he thought himself ready, he begged for an audience with King John of Portugal.

After waiting but a week, word came that the king would listen to Columbus, and a day was set for him to come before King John.

On the appointed day, Columbus presented himself and was led into the presence of King John, who sat not on a throne, but beside a table in a little study.

King John was a big man of good proportions. His ruddy face was long and red bearded. His hair was auburn, splashed with gray. His nose was prominent, and his eyes were bright and steady.

Columbus bent to one knee before him and

bowed his head. "Your majesty, I thank you for this privilege."

"Make yourself at ease," commanded the king. "They tell me you are a navigator, too—like so many others who request my ear since I undertook to handle such matters for my late father some years ago. And what islands do you intend to discover?"

"Sire, I have no one island for my goal. I propose to open a sea route to the Indies—to Cathay and Cipango—to go by way of the west towards the south and so discover great lands, rich in gold and silver and infinite peoples, and by that way to come upon the lands of the Indies and the kingdoms of the Grand Khan."

The king's eyebrows raised. "You're ambitious, Columbus."

"Sire, it is believed by all those who have studied these matters that we know but a fourth of the earth. All the rest is unknown. There are cities still unknown even to the learned—they have been written of by Messer Marco Polo and Cardinal d'Ailly. I have spent many years searching through all manner of writings. I've read the histories and the chronicles of journeys. I've read philosophy and studied other arts. Our Lord has opened my eyes and heart to know that it is possible to sail from here to the Indies, and He has opened my mind and will to make me ready to sail upon this route and open the way for Christians. I come to you on fire to be gone upon my journey."

The king's face did not betray his thoughts. "What is your plan, Columbus?" he asked.

"Sire, if I succeed in this mission, I would ask certain things. First, that I shall be armed a knight, with the right to wear golden spurs, and call myself Don Christopher, and my successors likewise. Next, that I shall be given the title of Grand Admiral of the Ocean Sea, together with all the privileges belonging to that title, including the governing power over such new lands as I may bring to the crown. Thereafter, I am to have one-tenth of all income coming to your majesty from such riches as I may discover or conquer. I should have also the right to contribute one-eighth of the expenses of every expedition to the new lands and to share one-eighth of their profit."

"Is that all?" asked the king with gentle irony.

"Sire, I ask this because what I hope to attach to

Portugal is not a small island—but many lands. And all depends upon my accomplishing the task I have set for myself. If the mission is not fulfilled, nothing comes to me."

"Except the ships you ask me to outfit and make ready for you, Columbus," answered the king. "You must know I am asked such favors every day. I do not dare to make a decision. I am in sympathy with you, Columbus, but I dare not permit my sympathy to overcome my reason. We know nothing of Cathay and Cipango save what Marco Polo has written. He may have imagined it all—who shall say?"

"Sire, I beg you, give me the tools to implement my hopes."

"A week from today, Columbus, you will appear before my advisers in these matters. In the meantime, I will submit your plan to them. We shall see."

Columbus left the king's presence well aware that King John doubted his wisdom. He was humbled. Perhaps he had hoped for too much. Perhaps he had asked more than he had a right to expect. But he did not think so in his heart.

A week later he stood before the commissioners

of King John. Two of the masters were almost openly scornful of Columbus; only Bishop Ortiz was considerate of his opinions. They asked Columbus many searching questions, and it was plain to him that these three men were learned in matters of cosmography—which is to say, mapping and descriptions of the earth—as well as many of the sciences.

"Do you really think, Columbus, that the sea is not wide and impassable?" asked one of the masters.

"I believe it can be sailed across. If I'm given the chance, I'll prove it."

"Do you honestly believe his majesty should risk his caravels on such a dream?" asked another.

"Sir, without the help of a reigning prince I cannot make the attempt. I had hoped that ruler would be King John, for is not Portugal first in all explorations?"

"Tell us, Columbus, where you conceived this idea," suggested the bishop.

"It came to me after many years of study. I've read all the books and records; I've studied the maps and charts. I'm convinced this is so. It was prophesied many times. I believe it's the Lord's will that I carry His word to the dwellers in the Indies."

They questioned him for hours until he was weary.

Then Bishop Ortiz dismissed Columbus with the promise that they would consider his plan and, in good time, make their recommendations to his majesty.

"Perhaps," suggested one of the masters, as Columbus turned away, "you have a map—a new map of these domains you wish to visit?"

Columbus hesitated. It was true. He had made maps based on the Toscanelli map. But had not some of these same men thought Toscanelli's map worthless? And what would prevent anyone from copying his map, just as he had copied Toscanelli's?

"I have a map," he answered slowly. "But it's for my own use alone, and drawn from speculation—not as a result of voyages already made—and thus of no use to others."

The master was not pleased. He said, "You are a master mariner, Columbus. Why aren't you content to ask for a royal caravel to explore the coast of Africa just the way Diego Cão has done?"

"Sir, anyone can sail to Africa. I mean to sail to the Indies. I would have nothing less."

Perhaps he should not have spoken with such firmness, he thought, after he had left the commissioners. Perhaps they would think him proud, even arrogant. Everything the master had said was true —he was, indeed, a master mariner. If he chose to continue in the African trade, he could be wealthy in a short time. Perhaps he could even be knighted and ennobled as Diego Cão had been.

But this would not have satisfied him. He had made a vow to God, and he was convinced in his heart that God asked no less of him but that he open a sea route to the Orient. How could he then do otherwise?

How long would he have to wait upon the will of the commission? It was now 1484. Columbus, with Filipa and little Diego, had moved back to Lisbon so that he could be near to the court.

As the weeks and months passed, Filipa, who had not been strong since Diego's birth, grew ill. To add to his worry about the king's commission and their delayed decision, Columbus had to assume the care of his young son in order to lighten his wife's burdens. Yet he spent as much time as he could with his brother, working on maps and charts, and he sat up late to study in his beloved books by the flickering lamplight.

Despite the disheartening delay, he grew daily more certain that he was right. He attended Mass faithfully, praying for God's help. He read over and over in his Bible, and when he came upon the words of Esdras, writing of the glories of God and of earth, His creation, and read, "Thou hast dried up six parts," Columbus was convinced that this was proof of his own belief that the sea covered only one-seventh of the globe, and that, therefore, the distance to the Indies could not be so far as the king's cosmographers held. Then Toscanelli—and he, also—were right, and those who went before and refused to set sail were wrong.

The year lengthened and turned.

Filipa grew steadily weaker. The doctors could not heal her. She remained in her bed for longer and longer at a time, and, finally, she could not rise at all.

She died quietly one day early in 1485. Columbus was deeply grieved. He had seen death approaching, but he had prayed and hoped until the

end. Yet he told himself that God meant to test
and try him, and He would not find Columbus
wanting.

There was yet another trial in store for him.

Soon after Filipa's burial, Bishop Ortiz sent for
him. Columbus hurried eagerly to the bishop's
home.

One glance at the bishop's face told him what
he feared to know. The commission had turned
down his plan.

"We have decided that it's impractical, Columbus," said the bishop. "We wish you well. Indeed,
we wish your goal could be reached, and I, no less
than you, hope for the bringing of the word of
our Lord to the people who live in the Indies. But
yours is not the way."

Columbus thanked him and left.

He was angry and bitterly disappointed. His
anger soon faded, but his disappointment did not.
What was he to do now? He could not hope for
help from King John. And if not from King John,
then from no one in Portugal. Yet he must have a
reigning prince to supply him with the ships and
provisions necessary to sail his perilous course
across the unknown ocean.

It did not take him long to decide. If he could not find help in Portugal, he must look to Spain.

One day he bade his brother, Bartholomew, a sad farewell. He promised to send for him as soon as he could. Then he took his son, Diego, and set sail for Spain.

4 Isabel the Catholic

HE landed at Palos. This was the port closest to that place in Spain where little Diego's aunts and uncles lived, and Columbus planned to leave Diego with one of his aunts until he had established himself in Spain. But, as the ship sailed into the harbor, he saw only a short distance away, well up a hill among the pine trees, the Franciscan friary of La Rábida. He decided at once to seek advice from the friars of St. Francis.

With Diego at his side, Columbus walked out of the village and up the hill. The friary was surrounded by a low wall, broken by a wide wooden door. Columbus rang the bell that hung there.

Presently the gate was opened by a friendly, middle-aged friar. "Father Juan Pérez," he introduced himself cheerfully. "Can we help you?"

Columbus, warmed by his friendliness, told him who he was.

"You travel from Portugal? Then you must be tired," said Father Pérez. "Come in and rest."

Made comfortable in the monastery, Columbus unfolded the story of his hopes and dreams. But he had hardly begun before Father Pérez halted him, saying that there were others who enjoyed hearing tales of marvels. He called the monastery doctor and an old Castilian pilot who was staying out his years among the friars. Before them, Columbus told his story.

He saw in their eyes none of the doubt which had been plain in the faces of the king of Portugal's commissioners.

"You must wait till our astronomer comes back to the monastery and tell him this tale also," said Father Pérez enthusiastically. "Father de Marchena will not forgive us if we let you go before he returns."

"I believe you're right, Columbus," said the old pilot. "Once I was sailing with an expedition out of Lisbon. It was in the time of Prince Henry—nearly forty years ago. We'd left Fayal Island and sailed southeast 150 leagues, driven by wind. On the way back we saw many land birds, and we knew them to be from some near land. So we sought it, and in that way discovered the Island of Flowers."

When Father Antonio Marchena returned, Columbus told his story all over again. Father de Marchena, an elderly man whose face was as austere as Father Pérez's was happy, listened with grave attention. At first Columbus could not tell how he regarded his story, but then he saw him nod from time to time and knew that he, too, took him seriously.

"This is an interesting theory, Columbus," said Father de Marchena. "It ought to reach the ears of our sovereigns."

"I know no one in the Spanish court, Father."

"Ah, that doesn't matter. I know them. The court is now in Seville—King Ferdinand and our gracious queen, Isabel, are giving thanks to God for the capture of Setenil from the Moors. I'll give you a letter to the Duke of Medina-Sidonia and another to the Duke of Medina-Celi, and trust to one of them to take you to the court so that their majesties may hear of your plan."

"Father—you believe in this plan!"

"Yes, my son. There's nothing in what we already know to say you are wrong. You may be in error—that is in God's hands. You may be right —that, too, is in God's hands. It would be a pity if anyone should prevent the glory of that discovery from belonging to the Spanish crown."

Columbus was filled with renewed hope and faith in himself. He had not dared to believe he would find it so easy to win the ear of anyone close to the Spanish court. He was eager to go at once. But then he thought of little Diego, now five years old—blue-eyed like his father, a sober boy who missed his mother and needed affection and care. Would it be fair to him to make him share the uncertainties of his father's life, in case neither of his aunts could care for him?

"My son, Diego," he said to Father de Marchena, "could he not find a home and a school here at La Rábida?"

"I'm sure that can be arranged," answered Father de Marchena. "I myself will speak with our prior."

Within a week, everything had been settled. Diego was to remain at La Rábida to live and study until his father sent for him. Only God knew how long that might be.

One day Columbus called his son to him. He sat for a long time stroking the boy's silken hair, sad at parting from him.

"Be a good, obedient boy, Diego," he cautioned him. "Do as you are told, and do not forget to say your prayers."

"Yes, Papa."

"And pray for me, too, a little. Some day I'll send for you."

He embraced him, kissed him, and bade him farewell.

Then he set out for Seville, which was not far from Palos.

Despite the friendliness and faith of the friars at La Rábida, Columbus had not entirely overcome his disappointment and bitterness over his treatment in Lisbon. He was not convinced, either, even by Father de Marchena's belief in him, that the Spanish nobles, much less King Ferdinand and

Queen Isabel, would give him the support King John of Portugal had denied him.

He entered Seville prepared for any turn of events.

He went first to see the Duke of Medina-Sidonia, a proud, haughty man, who was said to be the most magnificent in the whole peninsula and the richest man in all Spain. His lands extended from Seville to the harbor of Sanlúcar many miles away, below Palos on the south coast of Spain. Yet even this almost arrogant man, with his pointed beard and thin lips, his narrowed, penetrating eyes and his grand manner, was courteous to Columbus after he had read Father de Marchena's letter.

"You may be right, Columbus," he said after he had heard him. "I yield to Father de Marchena's superior knowledge in this. But is there anything now that is more important than the goal of all Spain—the conquest of Granada, the expulsion of the Moors from the last of Spain?"

"Your lordship is not interested?" asked Columbus.

"I am. I am, indeed. But not at this time. Come to me after we've seen the last of the Moors."

Columbus refused to be discouraged. But he had

no intention of waiting as the duke asked. The wars against the Moors had been going on for many years. By the time the Moors were finally driven out of Spain, he might be too old to make so dangerous a voyage.

He thanked the duke and set out for El Puerto and Medina-Celi.

Two days later he asked for an audience with the Duke of Medina-Celi. He sent in the letter from Father de Marchena and waited.

The Duke of Medina-Celi came himself in response to the letter, hurrying out of his chambers, followed by a retinue of servants. He was a younger man than the Duke of Medina-Sidonia, and his manner was enthusiastic.

"Come in, come in, Señor Columbus," he cried. "I'm always happy to know any friend of Father de Marchena's—and particularly when he comes with news of discoveries."

Columbus was almost overwhelmed by his openhanded manner. The duke took him by the arm and conducted him into his inner rooms from the forecourt where he had waited. He insisted that food and drink be put before Columbus, and only after he had eaten was he bidden to speak.

Then the duke listened raptly. Plainly, his imagination was seized by the daring of Columbus' plan to sail west to the Indies.

"I want to think of this for a while," he promised Columbus. "In the meantime I want you to become part of my own household. I'll pay all your expenses until such a time as I can decide what to do about this matter."

Columbus did not have long to wait.

Within a few days the duke sent for him again. He wished to ask once more about Columbus' plans. He wanted to be assured again that all would be as Columbus hoped. This time he asked many searching questions, and Columbus guessed that he had talked with mapmakers.

"But a little while longer, Señor Columbus," promised the duke.

A fortnight passed, during which Columbus was treated so well that he might have been a nobleman of his host's own station in life. Then he was sent for once more.

A glance at the duke's cheerful face told Columbus what he longed to hear.

"I've given this matter careful thought, Señor Columbus," said the duke. "And I've sent the order to grant three—perhaps four—thousand ducats to make three caravels for your purpose. Construction should begin in my yards here as soon as possible. Does this satisfy you?"

"It does indeed, my lord. I could not ask for more. But is there not something I can do—save to live here on your bounty?"

"Be of good heart, Señor Columbus. What we do, we do for Spain."

Columbus was overjoyed. He thanked his host gratefully, and that night on his knees he poured forth his thanks to God. Yet his joy was not entirely without flaw. He knew how princes and noblemen temporized and delayed. He knew, too, that no duke could grant him the titles and rights he longed to have. Only a reigning ruler could make such grants. But he resolutely crushed such thoughts and waited upon the day when work on the building of the ships would be started.

This was not long in happening. Almost every day Columbus went down to the shipyards in El Puerto and watched the ships take shape. The work went slowly at first, but, as the weeks passed, they began to grow in their stays.

There were, however, constant interruptions.

That year of 1485 was troubled with many wars and battles, with the tide running in favor of Spain. In March King Ferdinand and Queen Isabel had left Seville and gone to Córdoba to establish a new base of operations there. At once, the armed forces of Spain began to gather at the new base for the spring campaign. Like all the other grandees of Spain, the Duke of Medina-Celi went to Córdoba. And, like all the others, he wished to take part in every battle. He fought at Coín, at Cártama, at Benamaquex. After these cities had fallen to the Spanish soldiers, he went on to fight at Ronda and Marbella. And during his absence from El Puerto, work on the ships lagged.

In autumn of that year, the river El Puerto rose as a result of heavy rains. The shipyards were flooded, and, for many weeks, no work could be done there, even after the duke had returned from the battles in which he had taken part.

Columbus noticed, too, that on his return the Duke was preoccupied and brooding. After waiting in vain for word from him, he asked and was granted an audience.

"My lord," he said, "have you begun to doubt the wisdom of our plan?"

The duke shook his head. "No, Señor Columbus —only of our proceeding without speaking to the queen. With your permission, I'll write to her and tell her of your dreams for the Indies."

"It should be so," agreed Columbus.

The year was now drawing to a close. Just before Christmas, Columbus sent a long letter and a package of gifts to his son, Diego, at La Rábida. In return, he had a good report of his son's progress in his studies. The Franciscan friars were well pleased with him and had grown fond of him, for he behaved well and studied hard.

A week later Columbus had word from his patron, now once again away from his estates in El Puerto.

"Señor Columbus," the duke wrote, "I wrote to her majesty of your desire to sail west to the Indies. She replied that I was to send a report to her in as much detail as I knew. This I did. She has now written to say that she has sent the report on to her chief treasurer and accountant, who is now in Córdoba, while their majesties are in Madrid. Will you, therefore, lose no time in presenting yourself to this learned man? I wish you Godspeed and trust that our Lord attend your plans."

Columbus was ready to take any course which might bring him closer to his goal. The many delays of the past year had cost him a full twelve months. He would soon be thirty-five—and the years of his middle age were not far away. Then he would be too old to risk a long voyage. He must be on his mission soon.

He went at once to Córdoba.

The chief treasurer and accountant of King Ferdinand and Queen Isabel received him, listened to him, and questioned him, especially about the wealth Columbus hoped to find in the Indies, for the campaign against the Moors took more money than their majesties could raise without borrowing from the moneylenders.

Without telling Columbus how he felt about his plan, he forwarded it by opening another door to him. This time it was one close to the king and queen—no less than that of Don Pero González de Mendoza, archbishop of Toledo, cardinal of Spain, who was the chief adviser to their majesties. He was a member of the illustrious house of Santillana, and was a man of great power and intelligence.

Cardinal de Mendoza received Columbus in his splendid palace in Toledo.

"Speak to me of your plans, Señor Columbus," he commanded. "I have seen what the Duke of Medina-Celi has written, and I have heard all you have said to our treasurer."

Once again Columbus spoke of his dreams and hopes, of his vow and his conviction that he was destined to serve God in fulfilling his plan to reach the Indies and bring the Indians to Christianity. He said brave words of his fearlessness in the face of the dangers of his voyage, and boasted a little of the wealth to be found in the Indies. Had not Messer Marco Polo written of this wealth? Indeed he had.

But he spoke most of all of the converts to be made among the heathens there. And he spoke of that land of which Marco Polo had written—a Christian land ruled by one Prester John. Could not the Spanish Christians unite with these Christians and win back the Holy Land?

The cardinal asked but a few questions. "Do you have a map, Señor Columbus?"

"Your Eminence, I have shown it to few people. I will show it to you."

Cardinal de Mendoza studied the map carefully. He asked for some explanations, which Columbus made. He appeared to be satisfied that Columbus ought to be heard.

"I will arrange for you to speak to their majesties," promised the cardinal. "Take lodgings where I can reach you."

Thus it was that on May Day of 1486, Columbus stood on a broad plain outside Córdoba, where the Spanish armies were gathering for the spring campaign. He stood before the royal tent, where on a dais below the flying banners and flags, waiting upon his words, sat Ferdinand, king of Spain, and Queen Isabel, already widely known, because of her devotion to Christ, as Isabel the Catholic.

5 The Long Delay

KING Ferdinand was neither short nor tall. He was a man of medium weight and though, like the queen, he was now in his forties, his hair was still very dark and straight with no sign of grey in it. His eyes were friendly, and he gazed curiously at Columbus.

Queen Isabel stood almost as tall as the king, and she was more fair than he. Her eyes were both green and blue. Her face was beautifully proportioned, and her gaze was clear and challenging. It was she who spoke and made a sign for Columbus to feel free to speak in answer.

"We have promised Don Pero to listen to what you have to say, Señor Columbus," she said. "Speak."

Columbus rose from the knee to which he had fallen in homage and began to tell the king and queen of his dream to voyage to the Indies by way of the western sea. He spoke with great fire and enthusiasm, and, as his voice fell to ear, it seemed to bring to life the Orient of which he spoke and the sea routes across the unknown. Columbus saw that the queen leaned forward a little, as interested as he hoped she would be. The king, too, listened thoughtfully. Neither interrupted until he had finished.

Then Queen Isabel said softly, "This talk of degrees and meridians tells us little, Señor Columbus. Have you brought charts and maps with you —or do you lack them?"

"No, your majesty—I have them here."

Columbus unrolled his maps and charts and laid them before them. The king and queen bent over them as eagerly as any navigator would have done, though they looked at them without a navigator's knowledge. They gazed a long time. Then the queen signaled to him to remove the maps and charts.

"We're not competent to judge in these matters, Señor Columbus," she said, after Columbus had rolled up his charts. "But we are favorably disposed toward your plan. To that end you may rely upon us. We shall appoint a royal commission of those men in our realm who are expert in such matters as these. We shall wait upon their decision and then make our own. Meanwhile our war upon the Moors demands our most urgent attention."

Columbus murmured his thanks and accepted his dismissal. Though he had hoped that another commission would not be necessary, he was flattered that a special commission was to be appointed solely to judge his claims and study his conclusions.

Columbus soon learned that the commission had been appointed. It was composed of astronomers, cosmographers, mariners, and philosophers. Its chairman was no less a man than the queen's confessor, Father Hernando de Talavera, who was known all over Spain as a saintly man. Columbus learned also that the group would meet at Salamanca, where there was a great university at which any question they might face could be answered. In this city, too, there were maps and reference books, as well as learned men who could be called upon for advice.

As soon as he could do so, Columbus went to Salamanca. He sent word to Father de Talavera where he might be found and waited for notice to appear before the commission of inquiry. He did not intend to wait idly, however. As soon as he had notified Father de Talavera about his lodgings, Columbus went to the University of Salamanca to study in renewed preparation for the voyage he knew he must make.

There one day a tall, rotund Dominican priest with a lean, hawk-like face, stopped at his side.

"I'm told you are Señor Columbus," he said.

"Yes, Father."

"I'm Father Diego de Deza, professor of theology at the university, and, since earlier this year, a member of the commission appointed by their majesties to inquire into your claims."

"I still wait to hear from the commission, Father."

Father de Deza sat down leisurely. "You will

wait, Señor," he said. "But it is I who am impatient. Tell me now a little of your dreams of reaching the Indies."

Columbus did so. He was never reluctant to talk of his proposed voyage into the unknown.

"I have long thought in this manner myself," confessed Father de Deza when Columbus had finished. "I believe this is possible, Señor. I will do all I can for you."

They talked for a long time. When he rose to go, Father de Deza extracted Columbus' promise that he would come and see him soon.

But, despite his visits to Father de Deza, despite his studies, Columbus found time heavy on his hands. He was a man of action. He wanted to be up and about his mission; yet he must sit and wait, and wait, and wait. The summer gave way to autumn, and the autumn, in the same remorseless way, turned to winter. Still Columbus waited, almost in despair, for each year that passed made it seem more likely that someone else would discover the western sea route to the Indies while he waited in vain for the support which would make it possible for him to set sail.

Finally, late in December of 1486, Columbus

received notice to appear before the Talavera commission, "and be prepared to answer such questions as we shall deem fit to ask, and to submit any further maps or charts made by your hand in support of your claims."

Columbus went, filled with misgivings.

The Talavera commission sat at a long table. At its head sat the saintly Father de Talavera, who spoke for them all.

Columbus spread his maps and charts before the members of the commission. Being already familiar with his claims, they had no need to hear them again. So Columbus waited only for the questions he knew must come. They were not long in coming.

"These islands," said one of the learned cosmographers, gesturing toward Columbus' maps, "you've labeled them 'Antilia' and other such names—have you seen them?"

Columbus was forced to admit that he had not. "I have but read of them in other accounts."

"Were these the recorded documents of eyewitnesses?" asked another.

"No, sir."

"A dream, based upon a speculation, arisen from a legend," said yet another.

Father de Deza interposed. "But a possibility."

"Remote, remote," said another.

Father de Talavera interrupted. "My son, do you believe in your heart in this dream?"

"With all my heart, Father. With all my soul— for I have made a vow, and I have had many signs, I believe, come to me from God to persevere on my course."

"I see," answered Father de Talavera.

Columbus discovered no sympathy in the chairman of the commission; but neither did he see trace of enmity. Yet there was little response among them like Father de Deza's frank approval. All seemed to him skeptical except Father de Deza; all were filled with doubt, scornful of his maps, and distrustful of his claims.

The questions continued for hours. At the end of that time there was still no decision. Columbus was free to go, without knowing how the commission would decide.

He settled himself to wait again.

In January, he received word that he was to be given a fee of twelve thousand maravedis a year until the matter he had proposed was settled. This Columbus interpreted as the work of Father de Deza on his behalf. But at the same time he recognized in this act another discouraging fact—the Talavera commission was far from a decision on his voyage. He tried to believe that he was wrong, but time only proved him right.

As winter passed once more, and spring came, Columbus chafed at remaining in Salamanca. From Father de Deza he learned of the long arguments between members of the commission, of the many points still to be considered by the members. Father de Deza's guess that it would be "many months" before the commission made its report determined Columbus to leave Salamanca.

He paid Father de Deza a farewell visit and told him he planned to go back to Córdoba.

"I won't try to urge you to stay here," said the friar. "But keep in touch with us at all times. We move slowly, but with great care. That is our obligation."

"I understand that, Father. But you, too, will understand my impatience. I've waited so long— and I grow older yearly."

Father de Deza nodded sympathetically. "I'll keep on trying to do what I can for you—both here and at court, for, as you know, I was appointed tutor to Prince Juan last year while the court was at Salamanca."

Columbus was comforted by Father de Deza's unwavering belief in his plan to sail west to the Indies. If only there were others on the Talavera commission so favorable to him!

Columbus returned to Córdoba in anguish. There was nothing he could do to hurry the commission, and he could go nowhere else. He considered once again appealing through Cardinal de Mendoza to the king and queen, but this was certain to be useless because they would very sensibly tell him to wait on the report of the commission. Meanwhile, he had to sit anxiously idle, watching his years slip by and the possibility of success in his voyage grow more slender.

He went to an old friend he had known since his first visit to Córdoba years before. There he poured out all his troubles. His friend's cousin, a young and beautiful girl named Beatriz Enríquez, was especially understanding, and, as the days passed, Columbus turned more and more often to her. She never tired of hearing about his dreams, and she spent hours at his side.

For a while Columbus was comforted. Beatriz took his brooding mind from the commission's delay, and, as he grew more fond of her, his love for her softened his disappointment a little.

The year passed. It had been a difficult one, indeed, for the payments promised by the royal treasury had often been delayed and were sometimes of lesser amounts than they should have been. There were days when Columbus had to beg food and money in order to live; this added to his grief and wounded his pride. Sometimes it seemed to him that the trials put upon him by God had no end.

The next year, 1488, was no better. The Talavera commission still made no report, though Columbus learned by letter from Father de Deza that the members still discussed his plans very learnedly. He determined that he could no longer sit and watch his life flow past and his dream grow dim. Perhaps the king of Portugal would now be interested.

Columbus had kept in touch with all the voyages and explorations made by the Portuguese. He knew that John II was anxious to reach the Indies by sea, for the king had again authorized a voyager, Bartholomew Diaz, to search for a route to the Indies around Africa.

In late spring, Columbus wrote to King John. He asked whether the king would like to hear again of his plan to sail to the Indies by way of the western sea. At the same time he asked for safe conduct if he should come to Portugal. He was afraid that, having copied the Toscanelli map, he might be arrested for having done so.

King John replied within a month to say that he was indeed interested in learning more of Columbus' plan. He promised him he would not be arrested and asked him to come to Lisbon immediately, so that they might talk about plans to make the voyage.

Though he was eager to go, two reasons prevented Columbus from leaving at once. For one thing, he did not have enough money to make the journey to Lisbon; he needed to beg until he had collected enough. For another, he wanted to wait until his second child was born to Beatriz before he took leave.

The money came to hand readily enough. And on August 15, a son, whom they named Fernando, was born to Columbus and Beatriz. As soon thereafter as he could do so, Columbus left for Portugal. He went directly to his brother, Bartholomew.

"I thought you'd be back," cried Bartholomew at sight of him. "The king thinks of nothing but voyages of discovery. The time to strike is now."

"This time let's plan so that, if he fails us, we'll be ready to go somewhere else."

"But where, Christopher?"

"There are other princes. I'll go back to Spain and wait on that snail-paced commission while you can go to Henry VII in England, or to Charles VIII of France."

"Will you go to see King John now?"

Columbus shook his head. "I want all my plans to be perfect. I must redraw some of the maps and charts which the Talavera commission still has."

"But that will take time."

"Two months, perhaps—then we'll go to the king."

Two months passed and December came.

And with December came Bartholomew Diaz, sailing his three caravels up the Tagus to Lisbon. Word of his near success spread on the wind through the city. He had sailed around the south cape of Africa and was far up the east coast when his men had persuaded him to turn back. But the Indies were within reach. And it was plain to Christopher and Bartholomew that King John would no longer be interested in another sea route, having found one.

The two brothers immediately put their plans into execution. Bartholomew bade his brother an affectionate farewell and set out for England. Christopher returned to Spain, and to Castile, where Queen Isabel, learning of his arrival, sent him an open letter he could show to officials. The letter commanded them to give Columbus board and lodging on his way to the court, which was now in camp before Baza, under siege by the army of Spain.

Columbus went to Baza, but there was nothing for him from the king and queen save hope for a favorable report from the Talavera commission. On this all three—king, queen, and Columbus—must wait.

Again he waited—as long as he had already waited—almost two years. Then, late in 1490, the Talavera commission at last made its report. Columbus learned of it from the queen herself.

"I fear, Señor Columbus, that the authorities disagree with you," she said. "They believe your plan rests on a weak foundation, and that its achievement seems to educated men uncertain and unlikely. They believe such a voyage as you propose would take at least three years to accomplish, even if the ships could return. This they think is to be doubted, for the sea is much greater than you suppose, and perhaps is not to be navigated. And they doubt that God would allow any uninhabited lands to be concealed from His people for so long."

"And longer still," Columbus cried out, "if it lies with such men as these who lack faith and vision. I know I can find this route, your majesty!"

"And they say you cannot. But do not despair, Señor Columbus. We are now so much troubled over our war with the Moors. Apply to us again when the war is done."

With that Columbus had to be content.

6 Columbus Sails for Spain

LATE in 1491, Columbus arrived at La Rábida. Father Pérez and Father de Marchena were astonished to see him.

"I've come for Diego," he said.

"But the voyage!" protested Father de Marchena.

Columbus smiled ruefully. "I waited four years for the Talavera commission to report. It came to nothing. I've waited a year since then. Now I must go elsewhere. Diego is now eleven—he's able to come along."

"You're tired," said Father Pérez soothingly. "Rest a little here. We have a visitor coming today who may interest you—a man who has sailed the seas to Italy and Guinea and the Canary Islands. He lives in Palos and owns his own caravel as well as other sea craft."

"Why should he interest me?"

"Because he, too, believes in these undiscovered lands of yours. He heard of them from no less a person than the mapmaker for Pope Innocent VIII. His name is Martín Alonzo Pinzón."

Once again the hope of making new discoveries caught Columbus. "I'll talk with him," he decided.

Father Pérez then brought his son Diego to him.

Columbus stood gazing at the boy in astonishment. Could this be his son? This boy grown twice as tall as he had been when he left him, with his curly hair red like his father's now, and his eyes as blue as the sky. The boy looked at him as if he had almost forgotten him. But how could it be otherwise when all this time his father had not been to visit him, driven as he was by his dream of crossing the western sea?

"My son—Diego—don't you know your father?" he asked gently.

The boy nodded dumbly, uncertain still. But he did not retreat when Columbus advanced upon him and embraced him.

"We have so much to talk about, Diego," said Columbus.

While father and son talked and made plans for the future, Father Pérez sent word to Pinzón to come and bring the map given him by the Pope's astronomer.

The sea captain came, eager to meet Columbus. He was a grizzled man of middle age, and the two of them were not together for more than a few minutes before Columbus saw in Pinzón a kindred soul. And when Pinzón unrolled his map, Columbus was astounded—for the map drawn by the Pope's astronomer was much like his own, showing lands neither had ever seen but only believed were there.

"Pinzón," declared Columbus, "if I sail—if God wills this—you must sail in my company!"

"If it is God's wish, I will go gladly," answered Pinzón.

Father Pérez, meanwhile, hastened to write a

letter to Queen Isabel to tell her of Columbus' determination to seek help elsewhere. He assured her again of his own faith in Columbus' plan, pointing out how similar it was to that of the Pope's astronomer. He sent it to court by special messenger.

Then he set himself to blunt Columbus' decision, to keep him at La Rábida until the queen could reply. He raised objections to every place to which Columbus wanted to go. Portugal, he said, "already has enough explorers." And Henry of England was difficult to convince, while Charles of France was "all talk and little sailing."

In a fortnight a message came from the queen to Columbus asking that he be of good hope and wait until she could write to him. At the same time, Queen Isabel commanded Father Pérez to appear at court.

Father Pérez obeyed at once, leaving Columbus to embroider his plans with Pinzón. Columbus waited reluctantly; he could not take the chance of missing an opportunity. He did not know what Father Pérez had told the queen, but he wondered if he had not mentioned Columbus' copy of the Toscanelli map, which had been shown to no one but the two friars of La Rábida.

Another two weeks went by. Then one day a messenger came from court bearing a letter from the queen to Columbus. He carried, also, twenty thousand maravedis in florins. These, too, were for Columbus. The queen ordered Columbus to come to the court, and added, "I send these florins so that you may dress in a manner befitting your station, and buy yourself a beast to ride without delay, to present yourself to us as soon as you can."

Because the Spanish armies had reached the last great Moorish stronghold, Granada itself, the court was in camp at Santa Fé before Granada. It stood on a little hill from which one could look upon the scene of the siege. The royal tent was surmounted by flags and banners, but above them all flew the banner and cross of Spain.

The king and queen sat enthroned under a canopy stretched far out to shield them and all around them from the hot sun. Columbus came to one knee before them.

Queen Isabel signaled him to rise. "Come forward, Señor Columbus."

When Columbus stood at the foot of the dais, the queen spoke again. "We have had a new commission study your plans, Señor Columbus, and we have been made aware of their merit. We would know your terms."

The long delay Columbus had suffered emboldened him to ask for even more than he had asked of King John. He mentioned all those earlier conditions and added one other. "I shall expect to be made viceroy of all such lands discovered by means of this expedition, now or upon following voyages."

"You ask half a kingdom," said Ferdinand.

"Sire, if I ask it, it is because I expect to add so much to the crown of Spain that what I ask is but a very small part of the whole."

The queen was frankly astonished. She made no effort to hide her displeasure.

"Are you not prepared to accept anything less, Señor Columbus?" she asked gently.

"Your Majesty, I am not. I have waited a long time to make this voyage. Its dangers are very great."

Queen Isabel raised her hand in a gesture of dismissal. "Leave us, Señor Columbus. It is our wish that you remain in our camp until we've had time to think on this."

Day now followed day with hot insistence. The armies pressed the siege of Granada. The city fell, and the banner and cross rose proudly over the Alhambra.

Only then did word come from the king and queen. Columbus' demands were too great. Their majesties had reluctantly decided that Spain could not afford such an expenditure, in addition to the cost of meeting Columbus' other demands.

He was free to go elsewhere.

Once again Columbus was in despair. The year was 1492—sixteen years since Columbus had made his vow to serve God by bringing His word to the peoples who dwelt across the western sea! Now once again he was on the road in search of someone to sponsor his dream.

He left Granada with a heavy heart. The glory of Spain's successful war against the Moors was still fresh before his eyes. The banner and cross flew high over Granada. Here all Christendom had triumphed. And here, in this Christian country, under its most Catholic majesties, he should have found a haven for all his dreams.

He rode away from the city, turning but once

to look back at the fluttering flags and banners. He sighed and rode away on that beast the queen had given him to come to Granada.

Eight miles out of the city, just as he was crossing the bridge of Pinos, Columbus heard a horseman approaching rapidly from the direction of Granada. He was still on the bridge when the horseman rode up—one of the queen's guards.

"Señor Columbus," he called out breathlessly, "Her majesty has changed her mind. She wishes you to return at once. Don Luis de Santángel has agreed to supply money for your expenses."

Christopher turned at once. Again he was convinced God had intervened in his behalf.

Now that the fulfillment of his goal was within reach, Columbus determined to make up for the long delays he had suffered. Armed with the royal order sending him on his voyage, he hurried to the city of Palos, which had been commanded by the king and queen to supply him with caravels to carry him across the western sea. He also carried letters from their majesties to the Grand Khan of Cathay and other rulers Columbus might meet on his voyage.

It was now almost June. Columbus was in haste to be gone, but nothing was ready. And in Palos he met with further delays until he remembered Martín Alonso Pinzón. He went to him and learned, much to his delight, that Pinzón had been making preparations for the journey ever since Columbus had left La Rábida. Pinzón promised that at least two of the ships were within sight and that he would see to it that a crew was gathered. They would need ninety men for three ships, in addition to the guests—officers of the king, some servants and friends—two dozen in all. As for the third ship, there was now in the harbor of Palos, said Pinzón, a fine ship named *La Gallega,* for which they could contract. Perhaps Columbus would, himself, pay a visit to her owner, Juan de la Cosa?

Columbus lost no time in going to the harbor. He found the *La Gallega* easily. She was a large ship of over 200 tons, with a big castle aft and a lesser one at the prow. She measured almost 120 feet, and her deck came to over half that length. She carried square sails, and her mainmast was higher than she was long. Columbus liked the look of her, though he decided to rename her *Santa María* in honor of the Virgin.

He sought out Juan de la Cosa, a burly, well-muscled man close to Columbus' age. There was no need to explain his mission; he had hardly begun when de la Cosa interrupted with a hearty laugh.

"Say no more, Señor Columbus. Pinzón has already prepared me. She is for hire. I'm not sure I like the idea of your voyage, but the ship can be had—provided I sail with her as master."

"Done," agreed Columbus, "save for one other thing—I don't like her name. I propose to call her *Santa María.*"

De la Cosa shrugged and grinned. "Call her what you will. The men will have their own name for her. They always do—as you know."

"She'll be the flagship and I'll command her," mused Columbus.

"Wait till you see the others Pinzón has contracted for," said de la Cosa. "The *Pinta* is a smart ship—you may like her better."

But Columbus did not like her better. For one thing, she was not so large as the *Santa María.* The *Pinta* measured just over fifty feet in length. She, too, was square-sailed. And the third ship, the *Santa Clara,* known as the *Niña* because she had belonged to the Niño family of Palos, was trim and small. Columbus liked her appearance. She was a true caravel. This was the name given to a fast, long, and narrow ship, with but one deck, a flat poop, three masts, and lateen, or three-cornered, sails.

Arranging for the ships which were to make up the little fleet was the easiest of the tasks confronting Columbus. The Pinzón brothers, being wealthy, not only had these arrangements well in hand, but they also had loaned Columbus a half million maravedis to add to the more than a million supplied by the king and queen from the loan by Luis de Santángel. The tasks which remained to be done were sure to take a longer time. Men remained to be found for the crew, and the supplies for the long journey had to be gathered and stored —water, wine, biscuits, meat, fish, cheese, oil, vinegar, onions, and other vegetables—enough for six months, perhaps a year. And the ships themselves had to be outfitted.

Each ship had to carry arms. Small cannons called *bombardas* were put on board. They fired heavy balls of granite, though with such a noise and so much smoke that Columbus hoped it would not be necessary ever to fire them against pirates or other dangers. Each ship also carried *falconetes*, smaller weapons for firing lead bullets. The sails had to be painted; each sail had to show a great cross to signify that the ships passed on a mission of peace. The holds of the ships had to be ballasted with the ammunition necessary for the artillery. This stone and lead had to leave room for the materials needed for light and heat, for possible repairs, and for many incidental pieces of cargo—glass beads, mirrors, colored ribbons and caps, pins and needles, and similar goods to be used in barter with any natives they might discover.

While the Pinzóns recruited the crew, Columbus himself looked for men who might be of special service on the voyage. He hired one who could speak Hebrew, Chaldean, and some Arabic, hoping he would serve as an interpreter between Columbus and the Grand Khan of Cathay when at last they met. The king and queen sent a recorder whose duty it was to keep a record of all the wealth the voyagers might find, so that the crown would get its just share. They also sent a secretary with instructions to make an official record of discoveries.

As befitted a mariner who had contributed so

much to the voyage, Martín Alonso Pinzón was given command of the *Pinta*. His brother was named master of the same ship, while yet another brother was assigned the command of the *Niña*. Since the *Niña* was owned by the Niño family, Juan Niño served as master of this ship, and his brother piloted the *Santa María*. Columbus counted himself lucky to have so many experienced seamen with him. In addition to these navigators, the Pinzóns recruited stewards, caulkers, boatswains, seamen, and ship's boys from nearby towns, and saw to it that each of them was experienced.

All this took time. The pay offered—seven dollars in gold per month for each seaman, twice as much for officers, and ship's boys almost half as much less—was not enough to tempt many sailors to make so dangerous a voyage across the unknown sea. But as the weeks slipped past and the supplies were gathered, the men came in, and, at last, after so long a time, the three ships were ready.

June and July had passed. It was now the second of August, 1492. The ships stood proud in the harbor—their sides painted in bright colors above the waterline and pitched heavily below it. Large, gay flags flew, and the royal ensign of

Queen Isabel topped the mainmast. Each ship carried the special banner designed for the exploration —a green cross on a white field with a crown on each arm of the cross. Columbus stood for a long time looking at them that afternoon. Later, in church, he knelt in prayer for the success of his voyage and the fulfillment of his vow.

Then he gave orders for everyone to board ship that night. First, each man in the expedition confessed and received Holy Communion at the church of St. George in Palos, where Columbus had so often implored God for help. Then they made their farewells and went on board.

Columbus lingered. He was the last to rise from his knees in church that night. He was the last to board ship. It was past midnight—in the early hours of the morning of August 3—when Columbus boarded the *Santa María* and gave the signal to begin the voyage.

In the dawn of that morning the fresh winds swelled the sails of the three ships. The crosses stretched their arms as the canvas billowed out. On shore, the entire village had gathered, shouting and waving farewell. At La Rábida, the friars chanted and prayed for their success. The ships moved slowly down the Río Tinto on the ebb tide, swung past the Island of Saltes, out of the harbor of Palos.

The first sunlight shone a soft pink on their sails as the ships turned into that sea which no man had ever crossed. And Columbus, looking into the west, gave renewed thanks to God.

7 *Into the Unknown*

THE creaking of the taut ropes, the grinding of the pulleys, the cracking of the timbers of the caravels—all this was music to Columbus. Now he was captain-general of the expedition of which he had dreamed for so long. The voyage had begun, and he sat in the aft castle of the *Santa María* looking down to the sailors at their work below.

Much to the surprise of the masters, Columbus had set the course not west, but south by south-

west. He had been a mariner long enough to doubt
the wisdom of waiting for the strong head winds
to blow him across the ocean, and he rightly feared
the turbulent waters of the north Atlantic. So he
decided to sail first to the Canary Islands and then
turn into the west, aided by the prevailing norther-
lies.

The unknown sea lay ahead, and beyond it
Columbus was certain he would find the magic
lands of which Messer Marco Polo had written
200 years before. The sailors were in high spirits.
The adventure which lay ahead quickened their
imagination, and quite frequently they burst into
song.

Each day on shipboard was begun with a song
sung by a ship's boy. This was followed by a recital
of prayers. Every half hour, when the sandglass
which told the time was turned, the ship's boy in
charge of turning it sang still another song to God.
After sunset, before the first night watch, there
were evening prayers, begun at the lighting of the
binnacle lamp. Prayers were ended with the singing of the *Salve Regina* by all hands. It pleased
Columbus to hear, regularly each night, ringing
out into the surrounding darkness of the ocean, the

grave, stately words—*Salve Regina, Mater Miseri-cordiae, Vita, Dulcedo* . . .

The journey to the Grand Canaries was through familiar waters. It went almost without incident. The sailing winds prevailed for just enough days to take the ships within sight of the Canaries; then they became calm. The voyage to the islands had taken a week, but here, Columbus knew, there would be some delay.

The extra water casks had to be filled here, and additional supplies would have to be loaded—if they could be found. All necessary repairs would be made before they could sail again. Days were lost in the Canaries, but by the sixth of September, the ships were ready to set sail once more. On that day they weighed anchor, and Columbus gave the order for their course: "West—not to the north, neither to the south."

Three days later, the last land—the peak of Tenerife and the island of Ferro—sank below the horizon to the east. Now the sea stretched all around the little company of ships. Columbus knew that there was some uneasiness among the sailors at his course. They were accustomed to sailing along the land or toward it, not directly away from it as Columbus had ordered. Worst of all, for them, was Columbus' determination to stay on his course due west until they had reached the Indies; all knew that no one would shake his resolution. He did his best to comfort them by telling them he expected to sight land after 700 leagues, which seemed to them not too great a distance.

The three ships moved steadily westward before the easterly trade winds. The weather was sunny and cool. Every morning dew made the caravels fragrant as it dried, and the clouds along the horizon always carried the hope of distant land beneath them. The sea was like glass, and the air, for all that it bore the faint saltiness of the sea, was fresh. For ten days the ships sped along without a pause; then the skies clouded, the winds became variable, and rain began to fall.

According to the chart Columbus had made, they should now be close to the island of Antilia of which all mariners spoke, but which none had ever seen. Not only Columbus, but all his men looked for land. The captain-general ordered the deep-sea lead dropped, but gave the order to cease at 200 fathoms when there was still no land to be sounded. The ships moved more slowly now.

Rain soon ceased and presently the trade wind began to blow again. But it blew more softly and the ships made less time. They had been out many days, for it was now the end of September, and the men were becoming restless and ugly with doubts.

On the evening of September's last day, Martín Pinzón drove the *Pinta* close by the flagship and shouted to Columbus.

"What say you, captain-general?" he asked, when Columbus came to lean over the side.

"You saw the chart I sent you three days ago," answered Columbus. "Don't you think we should see land near here?"

"I do. But there is no land." He shrugged. "And the men are close to mutiny."

The sailors of the *Pinta* had crowded behind him, just as those of the *Santa María* stood in a half circle behind Columbus. At Pinzón's speech, all the men shouted their approval. Several voices called out a demand that the voyage be abandoned and that the ships return home.

Columbus faced them without fear. "Never!" he answered in a loud, clear voice. "You waste your time in complaint. I've come to find the Indies and I won't sail back until I find them."

Pinzón immediately supported Columbus. Grumbling, the men went back to their posts.

Columbus prayed long that night. He knew that the seeds of mutiny, once sown, would bear fruit unless land were sighted soon. Doubt of his wisdom had infected the men, and something must be done.

In the morning he sent word to Pinzón to come and speak privately with him.

When Pinzón stood before him, Columbus spoke of the rebellion which smouldered against him. "I know some of the men who speak most strongly against me," he said, "and no doubt you know others. We must act against them—but in such a way as to make no enemy."

Pinzón shook his head. "He who has no enemies has never done anything. The captain-general must be firm. Take these men who talk against you—hang them—throw them overboard."

Columbus was shocked. "We cannot do that. We need not."

"Then command me. I and my brother will take them and do it for you. We dare not return to Spain empty-handed."

Columbus shook his head. "No, no—we'll keep

peace. We'll sail ahead for a few more days. If we haven't struck land by that time, we'll talk over what we ought to do."

The first day of October, which was the day of Columbus' conference with Pinzón, was freshened by a stronger wind coming up in late afternoon. The three ships flashed forward. The wind blew all that day, all night, and all the next day. For four days after, the wind still blew with the same force.

Time after time men called out that they saw land, but each time it proved to be only a mound of clouds just barely visible over the rim of the earth. The men grew more surly than ever. But somehow news of the conversation between Christopher and Pinzón leaked through to the crews and made them think. If indeed they could get rid of Columbus, they would be hanged by Pinzón— and there were three Pinzóns to deal with, as well as other old friends of the Pinzóns from Palos.

On the seventh of October, Columbus was roused by shouting from his men. He burst out of the aft castle and saw the sailors pointing to the sky. A great concourse of birds was passing high overhead.

"Land birds! Land birds!" cried the men.

The numbers of birds flying into the south were incalculable. The flocks stretched from the northern horizon to the southern in an almost unbroken line. Their mass was as wide, Columbus guessed, as many times the length of the flagship. Since land birds seldom fly far out to sea, the presence of these birds was the strongest sign yet that they were close to land.

All that night flocks of birds could be seen flying across the face of the moon, which was now two days past the full. Columbus alternately knelt in prayer and sat beside his lantern in the captain's cabin, looking into his notes from Messer Marco Polo's story of his journey by land to the country of the Grand Khan. The names of those strange lands which might lie just ahead came to his eye as he had put them down—Cipango, Java, Yarcan, Kashcar, Campichu, Karakoran, Changanor, Clemenifu, Canbalu, capital of Cathay. There were many others whose names he had not copied. He slept that night confident that land was not far away.

Yet the next day passed without sight of land. More birds flew over, traveling west by southwest, and Columbus gave the order to alter course to follow the direction taken by the birds. Still another day went by, and once more the mood of the men grew ugly.

Columbus' attempts to quiet them were in vain. He pointed out how much each of them stood to gain if they found the Indies. He counseled them not to mutiny and revolt against the king and queen. But they shouted against him.

"Thirty-five days! No land for thirty-five days!" they rebuked him. "You promised us land before this."

"Land lies just ahead," he answered and turned his back on them.

But now even he was being troubled by doubts. Could his charts have been wrong? Could all his figuring have been made in error? Could his whole plan have been a mistake?

That evening the ships' captains and masters gathered to talk with the captain-general. As usual, Martín Pinzón, seconded by Juan de la Cosa, was their spokesman.

"Sir, we've traveled far beyond your reckoning. We don't know how much longer we can hold back the men. They grow very impatient."

"We fear violence, sir," added de la Cosa.

"What do you gentlemen think we should do?" asked Columbus.

"Sir—we have no heart for it—but wouldn't it be better to turn back while we still have enough supplies to see us almost home again?" asked de la Cosa.

"And you, Pinzón?"

"I, too, think we must soon turn back."

"The birds tell us there is land nearby," countered Columbus.

"That is so," agreed Pinzón. "But they don't tell us whether it's north—south—or west."

Columbus sat in silence, listening with a heavy heart to their arguments. They were persuasive. The captains and masters were in earnest. They felt, as keenly as he, the disgrace of returning without having reached their goal. They had begun to fear, though, as the crew had, that if they went farther and then, failing to discover land, tried to turn, they would run out of supplies long before they reached Spain again, and would be in danger of starvation.

Columbus could not answer this because he knew it to be true. But after he had listened, without saying much, and wrestled with himself and his desire to fulfill his vow to God and his promise to his sovereigns, he answered them.

"I wish to sail on, gentlemen. But if, within three days, we haven't sighted land, then I'll agree to return."

"Fair enough," agreed Pinzón.

Columbus spent most of that night on his knees, imploring God not to let him fail. Yet it seemed, on the following day, as if God had not heard his prayers. It was true that the wind blew stronger and more steadily. But the sea was heavier, too, even if the wind seemed fresher and less salty. Somewhere, Columbus hoped, there must be a sign.

Toward evening of that day a cry arose among the men. Presently one of them came to Columbus, bearing aloft a branch of a tree, still fresh and green with leaves.

"We picked it from the sea," he cried.

Columbus crossed himself. God had made him a sign.

On the deck of the *Santa María* the men shouted with joy. Where fresh branches were, land could not be far away. On the other ships of the little company there was equal happiness and relief, for other branches floated in the sea. And now and then, in the fading light, the men caught sight of flowers on the water.

All the next day branches and flowers could be seen on the water, and land birds were more common. Yet there was no land to be seen. The men, however, were now as confident as they had been doubtful and mutinous but a few days before. All hands expected to find land ahead.

One more day, according to the agreement with his captains. Columbus had no more time than that. That night he did not give the order to shorten sail and rest for the night. There was so little time left he could not afford to spend any of it resting on the heavy sea, though the northeast trade wind had grown to the force of a gale. The three ships moved along at as great a speed as any of them had yet seen. The *Pinta*, as usual in the past few weeks, was in the lead. Columbus signaled every ship to say that a steady watch should be kept. Then he resigned himself to God's will.

The sea grew rougher by the hour. Yet the sky was clear and the moon was to rise before midnight. The tension among the officers was shared by the sailors.

An hour before the rising of the moon, one of the sailors shouted, "A light! A light!"

Columbus, looking west, thought he saw it, too. "Like a candle—now here, now there," he said.

Then it was gone, though some others among the sailors swore that they, too, had seen it.

The ships pushed on. Spray shot high and fell over ships and men. The ships pitched and rolled. The moon rose and laid its sheen upon the endless water.

The night deepened. Midnight came and passed. The caravels dared the rough sea without lessening speed. The wind drove them fleetly westward, deeper and deeper into the unknown.

Columbus could not sleep.

At two o'clock, just as he had come out on deck, he heard the shouting of the lookout on the *Pinta*.

"Land! Land!"

Within a few moments Captain Pinzón's voice rose in a shout, too. Then came the signal agreed upon. A gun was fired from the *Pinta*. At the same time Columbus saw the *Pinta's* sails being shortened and the ship slowing.

As the *Santa María* came up, Columbus looked into the west. A white cliff rose out of the sea far ahead. This time it was no cloud—it was indeed land.

Columbus shouted across to the *Pinta*. "Five

thousand maravedis bonus to you, Captain Pin-zón!"

The crew burst into shouts of joy as Columbus ordered the ships to shorten sail and to keep to their present waters. Then their voices broke into the *Gloria in Excelsis Deo*.

Columbus gave his own thanks humbly to God.

It was the morning of October 12. Ahead of them now lay land. Columbus was confident it was that great strange country of Cathay which Messer Marco Polo had visited two centuries before.

8 The Strange Land

As soon as dawn broke, Columbus ordered the sails up. Ahead lay a long stretch of land which seemed to be an island, rather than mainland. In the early light, the sandy cliff shone pink.

The ships crept close to shore, then sailed south, looking for a harbor. They moved around the point of the island and up the other side. On the west coast they came to a little bay. Its shore beckoned to them past the barrier reef; it was of sand

reaching away toward trees and thick under-
growth.

Columbus ordered anchors down. Then the
Santa María lowered its boat and Columbus led
the way toward land. The boat flew the flag of
Castile while the boats carrying the Pinzóns flew
that of the expedition. As they drew closer, Columbus took note of the unfamiliar trees and birds.
The men shouted and pointed excitedly. They
were filled with anticipation of finding gold, but
most of all they were happy to be setting foot on
solid earth once more.

Large birds flying near shore screeched at their
approach and moved inland on powerful wings.
Other highly colored birds flew among the trees
growing back from the sandy beach. But Columbus looked in vain for some of the things described
by Messer Marco Polo. Yet he remained doggedly
certain that this was either the great island of
Cipango or one of the lesser islands in the sea of
Chin before Cathay.

The boats rode in to shore.

The men leaped out, shouting with joy, embrac-
ing each other in their happiness, praising God and
their captain-general all in one voice. Columbus

fell to his knees. By common consent, all the men followed his example and gave thanks to God for having led them safely to land.

His prayer of thanksgiving done, Columbus rose. He stuck the flag he carried into the sand and said, "We take possession of this island for King Ferdinand and Queen Isabel of Spain, our sovereigns. It shall hereafter be known as the island of the Holy Savior."

He had hardly finished when one of the men called out, "Look! Look! There are Indians!"

All of them turned and followed the pointing arm leveled toward the trees far up the beach. There, pressing out of the massed trees, came a group of natives. They came running, without fear, fanning out toward the Spaniards on the beach. Some of the seamen cried out in alarm and half raised the weapons they carried.

"Stay!" Columbus called out in warning. "They have no arms. They're peaceful."

The natives came up, eager and curious. They were without clothing, dark of skin. Columbus had never seen their like before, since they were not as dark as the Africans, but rather nut brown in color, as if they were white men long exposed to

the sun. Their appearance did not fit any description of men in the writings of Marco Polo, but
then Polo had gone to Cathay overland. He had
made mention of the islands before Cathay, but he
had not visited them, so how could he describe the
people who lived on them? Perhaps that was why
there was no mention of these natives in his book.

The Indians looked on in wide-eyed wonder. It
was plain that they had never seen white men before. They could not understand what the Spaniards were doing. They were fascinated by everything about them. They reached out and touched
their clothing. They stood in awe at the sight of
the secretary writing down the things that were
said, done, and seen.

Columbus led the way in mixing with the natives. He offered them glass beads and tinkling
brass bells. The natives, in turn, thrust forth in
friendship the colorful parrots they carried. But
they shied away when the Spaniards wanted to
touch the rings they wore in their noses. Not many
of the natives wore them, but Columbus was sure
the rings were of gold. Was this not additional
proof that he had reached the rich lands of the
Indies? Messer Marco Polo had emphasized the
riches of the Orient.

By signs he asked the natives what their land was called.

"Guanahani," said one.

Columbus could not recall such a name in Marco Polo's writings.

Now the natives mingled freely with the Spaniards. One of them touched the scabbard worn by one of the soldiers and drew forth the sword in it. He clasped it in his hand, then snatched his hand away. He had cut himself. At once he dropped the sword, called out to the other natives, and sprang away. The natives stood apart, looking suspiciously at the Spaniards.

Columbus tried to reassure them and allay their quick, superstitious fears. But even with the broken Arabic into which his interpreter translated his words, Columbus could not make himself understood.

At last he turned to his men. "We can't be far from Cipango. I propose to sail on till we find it, for we're surely among those islands said to belong to the Indies."

They returned to the ships and sailed out of the harbor.

Day after day they cruised among the islands. There seemed to be no end of them. Columbus landed on one after another. He named many of them—Isabela, Santa María de la Concepción, Fernandina. Sometimes they met natives; sometimes the islands were uninhabited.

Wherever they went, they looked for gold. They found none. Columbus could hardly conceal his disappointment. What would the king and queen say to him if he came back without the gold which he had boasted he would find? How repay them for the money they had invested in his voyage?

But there were other things to prize. Men exploring the islands came back with cinnamon and aloes. Columbus saw much cotton, and he realized that the great trees along some of the rivers of the islands would make fine lumber. He had his men bleed trees for musk gum. The Indian natives, he decided, would make good servants with only a little training, so he took half a dozen young natives who came out to visit the ships. Later he sent into the islands for a few women to go back to Spain with them so that the Spanish court might see what kind of people lived in the Indies.

For two weeks the ships sailed among the islands in search of the great island of Cipango. Columbus questioned the natives he had taken. One showed him places in his body where flesh had been torn away and told him it had been eaten by people called Caniba. "Caniba" sounded to Columbus like something belonging to the Grand Khan, and he was more than ever sure he was near Cathay. But where was it? The natives could not help him. They indicated that they had never heard of either Cipango or Cathay.

One day Columbus came to a very large island the natives called Cuba. The Indians referred to its middle as "Cubanacan." Columbus did not understand that "nacan" meant only "middle" in their language. He was certain they had reached the land of the Grand Khan. And Cuba was so large he was convinced he was at the mainland.

It was now November, and Columbus determined to lose no time in reaching the Grand Khan or his representatives. So he sent men bearing gifts into the interior and waited for their return.

They were gone three days. On the fifth of November they made their way back to the *Santa María*. Columbus was disappointed to see that they were not carrying gold.

"What of the Grand Khan?" he asked.

"We did not find him," answered the interpreter.

"Gold, then?"

"Nothing of that kind. We found only Indians."

"And some of them, women as well as men," broke in their leader, "carried the leaves of plants they smoked. They called it tobacco."

Once again Columbus was baffled. He did not care to learn more about the natives. Many of them now fled at sight of the Spaniards, for word of how he had seized the young Indians and taken them on board his ships had been spread among the islands.

Columbus sailed on, this time to another island the natives called Haiti. The natives of this island seemed to Columbus more intelligent than any they had yet met. He saw, when he walked among the crude dwellings they had, that they cultivated gardens. There were artists among them, for their mahogany canoes were sculptured. These canoes were so large that 150 Indians could ride in one at the same time.

Columbus presented one of the chiefs with a

shirt and gloves. Then he invited him to dinner on
board the flagship.

When the chief came, he and all the Indians
with him wore solid gold ornaments. They brought
golden gifts for the admiral, and Columbus was delighted. Plainly, gold meant little to these natives.
There must, therefore, be much of it to be had.
He questioned the chief, but he could learn little
from him.

After dinner had been served, Columbus had a
salute fired from the guns in honor of the chief.
Afterwards, he had the chief piped over the side
just as if he were a great dignitary. The chief was
pleased with the sound of the whistle at the piper's
lips.

Then began an earnest search for gold.

December was now already two weeks old. The
Pinta was gone one day, and Columbus knew that
Captain Pinzón was off exploring on his own. The
Niña and the flagship dropped anchor in Acul Bay
and were immediately sighted by the Indians who
lived there.

They came swimming out—hundreds of them
—though the ships lay three miles off shore.

Thousands more came in canoes. They scrambled up the sides of the ships and inspected everything like delighted children. Only when they had seen all they wished, men as well as ships, did they go back to shore the way they had come.

But word of the strange ships and the even more strange white men was passed rapidly from village to village while the ships lay in the bay. Within two days a native of more important bearing than those of the village nearby came to the flagship in a boat from shore. He showed by signs that he came with a message for the white chief.

Columbus ordered that he be brought on board.

The messenger managed to tell him that he came from a great native chief named Guacamari, who lived at a place called Marien, beyond Cibao, in the northwestern part of the island. He had sent the white leader a gift. With a flourish the messenger revealed a splendid belt, the buckle of which was made of solid gold. Guacamari, who had sent this gift, wished the white chief to pay him a visit.

Columbus accepted at once. Cibao sounded much like Cipango. Who could tell? Perhaps Guacamari was the emperor of Cipango?

The *Santa María* and the *Niña* were on the way before sunrise.

Columbus hoped to reach Marien by nightfall of that day, but contrary winds rose and drove the ships toward shore not far from the Caracol Bay where Guacamari's capital was. The men were exhausted on this day before Christmas, and even Columbus ventured to go to sleep, having had no sleep for almost two days and nights.

Just at midnight Columbus was awakened by the cry of the helmsman. He ran from his cabin. After him came Captain de la Cosa and others.

"Admiral, sir—we're aground!" cried the helmsman.

Columbus looked over the side. The bow of the flagship had grounded on a coral reef. He called out orders at once, thinking that the ship might be got off stern first. Boats were lowered and all hands hurried this way and that, somewhat confused. The *Niña*, aware of the flagship's plight, moved in closer. Even Indians, seeing the difficulty, came from shore in their canoes to help.

They worked for hours, but nothing that they did could save the *Santa María*. The ground swell had driven the flagship too high up on the reef.

Now the sharp coral heads were tearing her bottom. It was soon clear to Columbus that there was no hope of saving the ship. In despair, he ordered her abandoned.

When everything that could be saved had been taken off the *Santa María*, Columbus and all hands of the flagship went to the *Niña*. On shore, a company of Indians stood guard over the effects of the flagship.

On the *Niña*, Columbus sat alone, wondering why God had permitted this to happen to the expedition. He sought an answer in prayer. Christmas Day—and disaster! Surely it meant something! God's ways were strange but meant to be understood by His people.

In the little sleep that came presently, he tossed restlessly. But when he awoke he was sure that he understood God's will. He intended that Columbus establish a settlement at this place.

Columbus called all hands together and spoke to them. "I have pondered this accident a long time, and I believe we're meant to start a colony here. We can't all go back in the *Niña*—it must be intended that some stay here. But I would like to leave only volunteers."

Cries of "Let me stay!" and "I'll stay!" rose immediately.

"Don't count too much on the gold," warned Columbus.

No one, however, wanted to listen to warnings. "We'll make our fortunes now," cried one; he seemed to speak for all. Columbus counted thirty-nine men who wanted to stay. He appointed yet another to command them.

"We'll call this place Villa de la Navidad—because it is Christmas Day on which we suffer this disaster."

With the help of the Indians, they tore apart the *Santa María* and built a fort well up the shore. When it was finished, Columbus ordered that many provisions be left with the settlement. He gave them goods to trade and left them the flagship's boat.

"Go into the country," he commanded. "Make friends with the Indians. Treat them well—as Spanish gentlemen should. Look for a place to build a city. And seek gold so that their majesties may not be disappointed in us."

Guacamari, in the meantime, had learned of the accident. On the day after New Year's, 1493, a lookout burst excitedly into the cabin of Columbus.

"Admiral, sir!" he cried. "A large company of Indians is coming. They seem to be led by a great chief."

Columbus hurried to the deck to look. There, coming toward the *Niña* in hundreds of canoes, were many Indians. In the second canoe stood a tall, impressive chieftain who wore many gold ornaments. In the leading canoe an Indian crier called out in a loud voice from time to time. Columbus listened closely and guessed that the crier said, "Guacamari comes!"

So this was Guacamari. Columbus gazed at him intently and his spirits fell. He saw that Guacamari was not, after all, the Grand Khan, for he did not fit the description Marco Polo had set down. Just the same, it was easy to see that Guacamari was the most important chieftain they had yet seen in this country. Columbus gave orders that the chieftain and his immediate retinue be permitted on board.

Guacamari had brought a feast with him— enough for all the Spaniards. He gestured magnificently and had it laid out. Then, since he expected them to eat, Columbus ordered the men to partake of the meal, waiting first until the Indians had begun, lest the food be poisoned. After they had eaten, Columbus ordered the *Niña* to fire cannon balls through the battered hull of the abandoned flagship so that the natives might understand the might of their visitors. Then, bidding Guacamari farewell, Columbus saw the Indians off.

Disappointed in not having found the Grand Khan, he was determined not to wait and search longer, but to set out for home as soon as he could. Of the *Pinta* there was still no word. Perhaps she, too, was lost. Or worse—perhaps Captain Martín Alonso Pinzón had sailed on home ahead of him to lay claim to the glory that was Columbus'.

For two days Columbus fretted. Then, on the morning of the fourth of January, a favorable wind arose and he gave the order to set sail for Spain.

9 Homecoming

Two days out of La Navidad, the *Niña* was joined by the *Pinta*. Captain Pinzón came on board to explain where he had been for the past three weeks.

"We found gold at Cibao," he said, and showed Columbus some of it. "Then we heard that the *Santa María* had been wrecked—the Indians told us—so we hurried back."

Columbus' anger melted at sight of the gold.

"This will please our king and queen," he agreed. "Just the same, Martín Alonso, you shouldn't have gone off without saying where you were headed."

On the sixteenth of January, the two ships sailed away from land. The homeward voyage was rough.

Almost at once, the west wind under which they had sailed died away, and the wind sprang up again from the east. The ships found it hard to move against the wind, and Columbus was forced to abandon his plan to sail due east. Instead, he altered the course to east-northeast. Their progress was very slow, for the shifting winds constantly forced Columbus to order changes in the course.

In this way the ships moved all through January. Then, early in February, Columbus set the course due east. He was now well north of the course he had taken into the west, and he figured that if he could hold the course he had now taken, he should reach the Azores.

The ships moved without incident for ten days. Then a furious storm struck and separated them. The crews battled the high seas and the angry wind all night. Dawn brought no change; if anything, the storm raged even more violently.

Columbus called the men of the *Niña* together and spoke to them over the roar of the storm.

"Men, it may be God's will that we not return home," he shouted. "But I propose now that all of us draw lots for one to go as a pilgrim to the shrine of Our Lady of Guadalupe, carrying a wax taper. We will select chick-peas, one for each, and one will have a cross marked on it. He who gets that pea will make the pilgrimage if we are saved."

All hands shouted approval. Then the drawing began. The men fought the rolling of the *Niña* and the buffeting of the wind to make their drawings. When Columbus made his draw and opened his palm, he saw the marked pea in it.

"God's will!" he cried. "Now let us draw to see who makes the pilgrimage to St. Mary of Loreto in Ancona, a place where Our Lady performs many miracles."

The second drawing went to one of the seamen.

"Yet another!" cried Columbus. "To find who shall spend a night praying in Santa Clara of Moguer."

This time, again, the marked pea was Columbus'. Despite the chaos of the storm, Columbus was comforted. He felt that God meant him indeed to serve Him, or He would not have permitted Columbus to be twice chosen. Therefore, he reasoned, they would all be saved.

The crew, still not entirely satisfied, vowed to go together, clad only in their long shirts, and pray in the first church dedicated to Our Lady to which they came. Moreover, the day of the lottery was St. Valentine's, and all the men held this to be a good omen.

At dawn next morning land was sighted ahead. Columbus was certain that the land was one of the islands of the Azores. But the wind was so strong against the ship that it took three days for the *Niña* to drop anchor at the island. Columbus sent a boat to shore and learned that they had anchored at Santa María, the southernmost of the islands. Here there was a small hermitage dedicated to the Virgin Mary. Most hands left, as soon as they had fed on the fresh bread and chickens sent out by the islanders, to fulfill their vow to walk in their shirts only to pray before Our Lady.

In spite of Columbus' eagerness to set out for Spain, they were delayed by a misunderstanding on the part of the Portuguese captain of the island. Because he thought the Spanish ship had been sail-

ing to African land, which was under the juris-
diction of the king of Portugal, he and his men
arrested the members of the crew as they came
from fulfilling their vow. It was not until two
priests came to the *Niña* and talked with Columbus
that they were satisfied. The men were then freed.

Thus it was almost ten days before they left
Santa María. In all that time there had been no
sign of the *Pinta*. Columbus grew afraid that the
ship was lost with all hands. Yet there was a chance
that she, too, had weathered the storm, for Captain
Pinzón was known far and wide as a most capable
navigator, and his ship was heavily ballasted.

The *Niña* was not far past the Azores when
another violent storm fell upon it. Once again the
ship was in danger of being sunk. The men fought
the storm with valiance, but just a week after they
had left the Azores, the wind broke through the
sails.

Once more Columbus called all hands together
to draw lots to see which of them would go in his
shirt to Santa María da la Cinta in Huelva. Once
again—for the third time—Columbus himself was
chosen. As before, Columbus' fear of death gave
way to renewed hope in God. He was confident

God meant him to be saved, and that none of them would come to harm. He and his men plunged into the fight against the storm with renewed vigor.

The storm lasted for days. Sometimes the *Niña* moved ahead without sails. Once, by night, lit by lightning and in a pouring rain, Columbus ordered the mainsail spread. Though land was sighted, they could not approach too closely to it for days for fear of being dashed to pieces against it.

But at last the storm abated, and at dawn of the fifteenth of March, the *Niña* sailed past the Saltes. At noon the caravel came to the end of its journey in the harbor of Palos. The crowd which came to greet them shouted itself hoarse with enthusiasm. Columbus knew this was but a taste of what was to come as soon as the success of his mission was known.

Three hours later the *Pinta* sailed into the harbor. The rejoicing of the villagers was darkened a little by knowledge that Captain Martín Alonso Pinzón was gravely ill. Columbus, remorseful now for his occasional anger at his captain, went to stay with him at the Pinzón home, hoping for his recovery. Nor did Columbus forget the faithful

friars of La Rábida, who had never ceased to pray
for his success.

But Captain Pinzón did not improve. Within
five days of his return from his dangerous voyage
into the unknown, he was dead.

Columbus now waited upon word from his king
and queen. He had already written to them from
the Azores. He had told them in his letter that there
was much gold to be found, that the country of the
Indies was wealthy and fertile, that Cathay was
nearby, and that the natives were very docile and
ought to accept Christianity without question.

Ten days after Pinzón's death, Columbus had a
letter from his sovereigns. It was addressed to
"Don Christopher, our Admiral of the Ocean Sea
and Viceroy and Governor of the Islands which
have been discovered in the Indies." It made him
proud to read. He was commanded to appear
before King Ferdinand and Queen Isabel as soon
as possible.

Columbus set out at once for Barcelona where
the court now was. On the last day of March he
entered Seville, traveling like a prince. He was no
longer the unknown mariner come begging for
favors. He was now the Very Magnificent Lord

Don Christopher Columbus. With him traveled his Indians, who attracted the awed attention of everyone they passed. He carried some of the gold he had found. Each time he showed his gold Columbus' fame grew. It swept before him like a mighty wave. Wherever he went great crowds of people walked beside him, staring at the Indians and at the colorful parrots they bore.

His triumphant passage from city to city brought him to Barcelona in a month. The king and queen received him at once before the royal throne, which was set up outside in front of the palace so that all the court and as many of the Spanish people as possible might witness the event.

Columbus and his entourage were the focus of all eyes. The Indians, the golden masks, the pearls, the parrots, even the tropical fruit he had brought from his voyage—all were displayed and left to be seen while Columbus moved forward to fall to his knees before the king and queen.

The king, he saw, was thin and pale. He still suffered from the effects of an attempt on his life four months earlier. Queen Isabel was unchanged; she smiled to share his triumph. As Columbus came forward, both the king and the queen astounded the court by rising to greet him, hailing him as "Don Christopher Columbus, our Admiral of the Ocean Sea." Even more than this, they showed how much they favored him by offering him their hands to kiss, and by ordering a chair brought forward so that Columbus could sit while he spoke to them. Columbus' joy was complete when he saw his son, Diego, serving as a page to Prince Juan. But there was no opportunity now to speak to him, for the singers of the queen's chapel were singing the *Te Deum Laudamus*.

When the singers finished, King Ferdinand signaled Columbus to speak.

Columbus rose and addressed the court. He told of the wonders of his discoveries. He pointed to the Indians and the treasures he had brought back with him. He said that he was convinced he had discovered the many islands said to belong to the Indies.

"I came close, too, to the island of Cipango, and to that empire of Cathay written of by Messer Marco Polo," he asserted, "though I cannot say I have actually touched upon either. I have put up big crosses at the mouths of the harbors, where they can be seen from everywhere, as a sign that their majesties will hold this country as part of their lands, and mainly as the sign of Jesus Christ, our Lord, and the religion we serve."

"We are well pleased with our admiral," replied Queen Isabel. "We take pleasure in knowing of the lands which have been added to our domain. And we hope to take steps to bring them more securely under our crown, lest our rivals in Portugal claim them, and also to carry Christianity to them."

"To that end," added the king, "we desire that a second fleet be made ready under your command to return to the Indies and secure them for us."

"Sire, I am ready—nay, eager—to go back to the Indies as soon as ships can be made ready," answered Columbus.

The king and queen questioned Columbus for a long time. They seemed to be well satisfied with his answers. When they had finished, the king beckoned young Diego Columbus forward and sent him to his father.

Columbus embraced his son with tears of joy in his eyes. Diego returned his embrace with fervor. "I'm happy for you, Father," he said.

"Are you satisfied to be here, my son?"

"Yes, Father. Father Pérez sent me. At first I did not want to go, but now—they treat me so well—I'm glad I did."

"We shall see more of each other, my son," promised Columbus.

Diego went back to his post and Columbus once again faced his king and queen.

The king rose and announced, "The court will accompany our Admiral of the Ocean Sea to his lodgings."

Columbus rode at the king's side, with Prince Juan on his other side. Not far away Diego rode, too. Columbus' cup of joy was full.

After that day honors came in great numbers to Columbus.

He was asked to dine with Don Pero González de Mendoza, Grand Cardinal of Spain. There, for the first time, all the food Columbus ate was tasted before it was served, to make sure that there was no poison in it. This was proof of the greatness that had come to him, for only the great were in danger of being poisoned by food or drink.

The king and queen showered rewards upon him. In the middle of May, Columbus was granted the right to wear a castle and a lion in his coat of arms. These were the royal arms, and that the king and queen should grant him this right was evidence of how much they thought of him. A few days later he was given a gift of a thousand gold doblas and the right to lodge, with five companions, wherever he liked. Before the end of May, all the titles and privileges which had been promised him before he sailed for the Indies were confirmed.

Before the end of that month, too, Columbus received the royal appointment as captain-general of the second fleet going to the islands he had discovered. The orders he received also gave him the right to appoint governors for the lands across the western sea, which meant that Columbus could choose three persons, of whom the king and queen would select one.

In the meantime the second fleet was being made ready. Columbus was anxious to be gone. In less than two months the glory that was his was beginning to wear thin. He had begun to dream anew of the wealth of the Indies and of the power that would be his as the viceroy of the king and queen across the western sea.

The king and queen were anxious that he go
because the king of Portugal was also considering
sending ships to the newly discovered islands. In
Rome the Spanish representatives at the Vatican
had persuaded Pope Alexander VI to issue a bull
granting to Spain the Indies discovered or yet to
be found, in case the king of Portugal should be
inclined to argument.

To all this Columbus paid little attention. He
was more concerned with the men appointed by
the king and queen to make the voyage with him,
and particularly with Antonio de Torres, who was
named captain of the return voyage. Columbus
thought that he, though friendly, was most likely
a watchdog appointed for no other purpose than
to oversee the expedition. There were other men
like him, but without command or other authority.

Columbus had asked that 2,000 settlers volun-
teer for settlement of the Indies—enough, he said,
to build four towns. He also wanted to lose no
time in fulfilling his vow. To that end, priests
would be needed to carry the faith to the Indians
of the western islands. King Ferdinand and Queen
Isabel chose a Benedictine friar named Father Fer-

nando Buil to be in charge of the conversion of the Indians.

But before he could go on his voyage, Columbus had first to fulfill the vows made on board the *Niña*. In June, therefore, he went to the shrine of Guadalupe. He carried a five-pound wax taper and went clad in the simplest garments. For three hours he knelt in the dusk of the shrine, praying, shedding the pride which had come upon him, in homage to the Virgin. "Blessed Mother," he prayed, "intercede in my behalf. Do not let us fail. Pray for us that we shall be the vessels through which the word of God reaches those across the western sea."

One after another Columbus fulfilled the promises he had made to God. Then he turned to Cadiz, that white city down the coast from Palos, from which the second voyage was to start out.

There in the harbor of Cadiz the ships were being assembled. Once more the *Niña* was among them. And again the biggest ship was named the *Santa María*. Slowly the fleet grew until there were seventeen caravels in all. Seventeen crews were recruited to man the ships. Doctors, soldiers, craftsmen—200 volunteers eager to search for gold—

all came to Cadiz to set sail with the Very Magnificent Lord Don Christopher Columbus.

On the morning of September 24 the fleet sailed out of Cadiz into the no longer unknown west. In Columbus humility vied with pride.

10 Years of Exploration

EARLY in the morning of November 3, a look-out sighted land. Columbus immediately named the new island Dominica and called together all hands to offer up a prayer of thanksgiving. The crews sang hymns in their gratitude for an easy, rapid passage across the ocean.

Then there began a journey of exploration among many islands. Columbus named them—at first with devotion to the Virgin Mary and her

shrines—Santa María de Guadalupe, Santa María
de Monserrate, Santa María de la Nieve, Santa
María la Antigua; then with other names he
thought fitting—Santa Cruz, The Virgins, St.
John the Baptist. Sometimes he landed and took
formal possession of the land for the king and
queen of Spain while the secretary of the expedition put down all that was said and done so that
their majesties might themselves read it if they
wished.

Columbus had wanted to sail southward. But he
had worried about the men left at La Navidad ever
since he had taken leave of them on his first voyage.
So, since the colony of La Navidad lay to the
north, it was in that direction the fleet went.

All that month of November they sailed north.
Once, in the middle of the month, when they were
anchored off the mouth of a small river, the Spaniards surprised a boatload of Carib Indians who
fired on them before the white men could signal
their friendship. The Caribs who witnessed the
battle from the shore shouted in such anger and
looked so fierce that Columbus decided it would be
folly to land among them, even though their weapons were no match for those of the fleet.

Late in November the fleet came to the island of Española on which Columbus had established La Navidad. Columbus landed a party of his men to look for a site to establish a new settlement farther south than La Navidad.

They came hurrying back to the ship where Columbus waited eagerly. But at sight of their grave and somewhat frightened faces the admiral was filled with foreboding.

"What have you found, captain?" he asked the leader of the party.

"Sir—the remains of two dead men."

"Surely you've seen dead men before? Does the land look promising for settlement?"

"Sir—these men wore beards. Do Indians wear beards?"

Columbus' only answer was to shout orders. "Make haste for La Navidad!"

Dead white men lying on that strange earth! They could be none but Spaniards, for no one else knew of this land. And Spaniards had been left on Española. And the others? Columbus did not want to think of what might have happened to them, for he knew them all. But he was afraid, for, if it were possible for them to do so, the other

Spaniards would have given these two dead men Christian burial!

At nightfall of November 27 the fleet came to anchor in the bay not far from La Navidad. Columbus would go no farther, for he feared the dark, remembering the fate of his first flagship. He ordered flares to be lit, but there were no answering flares. He ordered cannons to be fired, but there was no reply to this cannon fire either. But later, after darkness had fallen, voices were heard from the water, shouting, "Almirante! Almirante!"

"They are Indians," said Columbus. "Fetch them aboard."

The Indians came bearing gifts. The interpreter Columbus had with him was one of the Indians he had taken on his first voyage. He had named him Diego Colón. Columbus called him forward to ask these Indians about the men at La Navidad. He stood by while Diego Colón and the Indians talked, waiting patiently for his interpreter to finish. At last Diego Colón turned to him.

"The white men are all dead," he said. "Guacamari, who sends you his greetings and these gifts, says that the Spaniards stole gold and troubled the

Indians, killing many. When they invaded Maguana, which is in the middle of this place, the Chief Caonobó took them and killed them. Then he attacked the settlement and hunted down all who escaped. They are all dead."

Columbus was speechless with shock. But this gave way to shame and disappointment that it should have been his men who broke the peace between white invaders and the natives. Father Buil suggested that Guacamari be captured and put to death as an example, but Columbus would not hear of it. Instead, he gave orders that La Navidad be searched and that burial be given to any bodies found. Only when this was done did the admiral order the ships east in search of a harbor and a place to settle.

Twenty-five days later the fleet anchored along the coast of Española, well away from the site of La Navidad. It was now early in January of 1494. Columbus himself went ashore. The land was high and not swampy.

"Here we shall found a city," said Columbus. "We'll call it after our queen—Isabela."

"Couldn't we find a still better place?" asked one of the captains.

"Perhaps. But we cannot delay any longer. Our provisions are running low. And our king and queen will expect most of the fleet to return before long with a report for them."

They set to work at once to build a city in the Spanish style. At the same time Columbus sent men to look for cargo to carry to the court. They brought cinnamon, pepper, sandalwood, parrots, and Indians. Columbus was disappointed, and he feared that the king and queen would also be. He selected two dozen of his hardiest men and called them together.

"Men, I am sending you into Española—to Cibao—under the leadership of Alonso de Hojeda," he said. "Your one purpose is to discover gold for their majesties."

The men cheered lustily. Gold was the object of their voyage. They went gladly.

They did not return empty-handed. De Hojeda proudly produced several great nuggets of gold.

"There's more," he said. "And I hope I may stay to look for it."

"We shall see," answered Columbus.

He sat down at once and wrote his report to the king and queen, asking for more food and supplies, seeds, clothing and some firearms. Then he dispatched twelve of the ships to Spain. The rest of them remained anchored off Isabela.

Early in the spring, Columbus led a triumphal march into the interior of the island. In one place he established a fort and left there fifty men. He selected de Hojeda to remain with them and take charge of the search for gold. The rest of them returned to Isabela.

But the old eagerness to explore soon took hold of Columbus again. One day he called his brother, Diego, to his side.

"I'm going among the islands, Diego," he said. "I'll leave you in charge here."

"I'd sooner go with you. I don't have much wish to govern."

"No. You stay. Remember only to be temperate and kind, above all, to the natives. Be firm in discipline. Do not be brutal."

Then he set sail in the *Niña*, with the *San Juan* and the *Cardera*, which were smaller ships. It was now almost May. Columbus had spent close to four months in Isabela, and he left behind him a well-built, fortified city.

West, then south, and again west they sailed.

Sometimes the perfumes of the islands crossed the water to the ships. In one place Columbus was fascinated by the sight of many red flamingos. In another, he was amused to see Indians using trained pilot fish to catch turtles. In many places he landed and made friends with the Indians.

Columbus pushed on to Cuba, always looking for evidence of Cathay. But as day followed day, and there was nothing to show that this was the land of the Grand Khan, he began to worry. He had told the king and queen he had found the Indies. Now he began to believe that Cuba was the mainland, and not an island, after all.

But he could not go endlessly on. The ships had been buffeted by sea and winds for a long time and they were in need of repair. Sadly Columbus ordered them back to Isabela, for he, too, was unwell.

When the little fleet reached Isabela late in September, Columbus was so ill and exhausted that he had to be carried ashore. Ill as he was, he recognized with joy a familiar figure who waited for him. He raised himself up in the arms of the seamen and cried out, "Bartholomew!"

It was indeed his brother. "I came with the supplies you sent for," he said. "I have things to tell you, Christopher—when we can be alone. How is this sickness?"

"I'm very weak and tired," admitted Columbus. "The doctor will tell us. Come to me after I've seen him."

After a prolonged rest had been ordered for Columbus, Bartholomew came to his rooms. "I don't want to trouble you, Christopher, but there's talk against you at court," he said.

"A man who succeeds always makes enemies—if only because he has succeeded where others have failed," answered Columbus.

"I'm afraid it's more serious than that," said Bartholomew. "Some who were with you on the way over complain against you. Father Buil . . ."

"And the others?"

"I'm not sure of them."

"Bartholomew—I can't govern while I lie ill. I'll appoint you governor here."

"We'll see what can be done," promised Bartholomew.

But Isabela and the colony did not flourish. The Indians would not work, as the Spaniards tried to make them do. Yet, if the Spaniards were to bring out gold in the quantity Columbus had promised the king and queen, the Indians would have to help find it. Nor would the Indians pay a tax in place of working. Instead, most of them left their settlements and moved into the mountains where the Spaniards could not find them.

When the captain-general of the fleet which had sailed to Spain returned to Isabela, he carried a letter from the king and queen for Columbus. The Spanish sovereigns told Columbus that an agreement with Portugal had been signed. They asked him, or his brother, to come home and help define the line which showed which part of the world belonged to Portugal and which to Spain, so that new maps could be made.

Columbus answered briefly that neither he nor one of his brothers could come. All were too busy dealing with the revolt against the Spaniards among the Indians. The revolt, indeed, had spread. Late in March of 1495, Columbus led an army against the aroused Indians. They took prisoner Caonabó —that chief who had slain the settlers at La Navidad—by the simple trick of persuading him to wear handcuffs, which he thought were ornaments. Columbus brought the chief back to Isabela, and from there sent him, together with 500 other Indians, to be sold as slaves in Spain.

Late in October of that year, while the war with the Indians was still going on, a new fleet of ships arrived from Spain. The expedition brought Juan Aguado—a dark, hot-eyed man—who rode out into the country beyond Isabela to meet Columbus returning from battle.

Aguado bent his head respectfully to Columbus. "My lord admiral, I have a letter from our king and queen to be posted in a public place."

Columbus broke the seal and read: "The king and queen—To all persons who are in the Indies on our mission, we send you now Juan Aguado, who is our butler. He will speak on our behalf, and we order you to believe what he says to you and to have faith in him."

That was all. Columbus handed it back to Aguado. "Have it posted where you wish," he ordered.

But Columbus was deeply troubled. He recalled the warning Bartholomew had given him months before. Trouble at court. Voices raised against him. Now here was a special envoy from their majesties with a letter addressed to all Spaniards—and no special word for him, their viceroy! Aguado had been sent to see for the king and queen whatever the reports had not carried. Columbus was humiliated.

His humiliation, however, did not blind him. He knew it was time for him to return to Spain. He ordered Bartholomew to found a new capital, Santo Domingo, on the south side of the island. Then, leaving him as governor and captain-general of the colony, with Diego as second-in-command, and Francisco Roldán as alcalde, or mayor, of Isabela, Columbus sailed early in March, 1496.

The two ships reached Cadiz on the eleventh of June.

Columbus went at once to Seville. This time he did not travel in triumph. To still the voices of his critics, he donned the simple brown robe of a Franciscan friar, and with only his Indians and his parrots, he went to stay with Father Andrés Bernáldez, chaplain of the archbishop of Seville. There he waited for the royal command which must precede his visit to the king and queen.

It came in July, after Columbus had had ample time to explain his voyage and his dealings with the Indians to Juan de Fonseca, the bishop of Badajoz, whom the court had appointed to inquire into matters in the Indies. Columbus was invited to come to court as soon as it pleased him.

He went, still clad in his Franciscan habit. His

retinue, however, was impressive. It was led by
servants carrying cages filled with the gayly colored parrots which screamed warning of his approach. The Indians went adorned in feather head-
dresses and ornaments, and Columbus had one of
them wear a gold collar of great worth. Columbus
himself, so simply dressed, with his beard now all
silver and he as humble as a petitioner, made all
who saw him think he had been wronged by his
critics.

The court sat at Burgos, waiting anxiously for
word of a fleet which had gone in stormy weather
to bring the Princess Margaret of Austria to Spain
to marry Prince Juan. Columbus appeared before
them humbly; this time there was no fanfare as
there had been after his first voyage.

"My lord admiral," said the queen, "we're
happy to see you safely home once more."

"And most anxious to learn of your success,"
added the king.

"Though we've been displeased in this matter
of your taking Indian slaves for us," continued
Isabel. "Is this just, in conscience? Are they not
also God's children, not to be sold into slavery?"

"Your majesty, they were captives, taken in

war—and so they could justly be sold as slaves."

"But who imposed the war upon them?" interrupted Bishop Fonseca.

The queen signaled for silence. "We will hear our admiral."

Columbus began at once to speak in his defense. But he spoke not only to say that he had sent slaves to make up for the lack of more gold. He also boldly asked for a new fleet so that he might search for a new world said to be south of the Antilles. He admitted that ships filled with gold had not yet sailed from Española; but this could not be accomplished overnight.

"But what is this," he cried passionately, "if not a shameful accounting of possible profit? Are not your majesties the most glorious princes in all Christendom? Have not other great sovereigns sent abroad ships to explore the unknown world? Is not even now Portugal preparing to send Vasco da Gama in search of this very world I believe awaits discovery? Do those who attack us think how much glory we have won for Spain in all the Christian world?"

The king and queen listened but gave him no answer.

Columbus left the court, convinced that God was punishing him for his sin of greed. But in a few days he sent to the queen an urgent letter saying that all would be well with the fleet carrying Margaret of Austria, for the wind had turned in the right direction and the ships should begin to come in to the port of Laredo on the following Monday.

This happened just as he had predicted. The queen was much pleased and impressed. Soon after the court learned that Vasco da Gama was indeed planning to leave Portugal for an unknown destination. Perhaps Columbus was right once again?

Columbus was even then visiting his two sons—Diego and Fernando—who were with the royal family. There word reached him from the king and queen that a fleet had been ordered made ready for the third voyage. Once again the Admiral of the Ocean Sea humbly thanked God for this sign of His favor.

On the thirtieth of May, 1498, Columbus sailed from Sanlúcar de Barrameda with six ships and crews and 200 men besides.

11 Failure and Disgrace

In the middle of July an unknown island was sighted. Columbus named it Trinidad, as he had vowed to do. His fleet had been sailing south, but now the heat was so great that their supplies of food had begun to spoil, so Columbus altered his course for Dominica to the north.

Bartholomew came out to meet him and was piped on board. After affectionate greetings had been exchanged, Bartholomew unburdened himself.

"Things are not well, Christopher. We already have a small rebellion. Roldán has taken seventy picked men and gone to the settlement of Xaraguá. Now he obeys no orders."

"He'll listen to me," answered Columbus confidently.

"It's worse than you think. I've come to believe, brother, we were meant to be explorers—not viceroys or governors."

"Don't talk that way."

"Nevertheless, you'll see . . ."

When he had landed in Española and had had time to see what was happening, Columbus began to think Bartholomew was right. He tried repeatedly to bring about peace. He set up a judicial inquiry and spent months trying to bring order back to Española. Persuasion, force of arms, commands—all failed him. In the solitude of his rooms he cried his misery aloud, "Oh, I am an unhappy sinner. I made too much depend on things of this world and not enough on God!" His prayers seemed unanswered, even unheard.

Matters did not improve.

Late in October Columbus sent slaves and treasures to Spain in five ships. As soon as possible after the ships had reached Spain and word could be returned to Española, Columbus learned of the displeasure the sight of the Indian slaves had given Queen Isabel, even though he had written that they had been taken in battle. He learned, too, that Bishop Fonseca had spoken against him.

Late in the following summer Alonso de Hojeda anchored a little fleet of ships off Española. He carried orders from Bishop Fonseca permitting him to explore all such lands as had not yet been discovered by Columbus by 1498. He thus had permission to explore without regard for Columbus' claims or privileges. Columbus was angered because he foresaw that this new division of authority might result in still further trouble.

Columbus' foresight proved to be true. De Hojeda took the side of Roldán and added to the woes of the Columbus brothers. The entire settlement suffered from this constant struggle for power, and the Indians, growing aware of the quarrels among the Spaniards, could not be made to co-operate.

At last, in despair, Columbus wrote to the king and queen. "I pray you, send me a learned man who can serve us here to administer justice. My forces fail me; I shrink and grow old."

Not until late summer in 1500 did Columbus learn that the king and queen had answered his request. Then a courier came to him while he was in the settlement of Concepción to say that Francisco de Bobadilla, a gentleman of the royal household, had come with letters from their majesties. From this courier he learned also that Bobadilla had taken upon himself authority that was supposed to be Columbus'.

He hurried back to Santo Domingo and was met by two representatives of Bobadilla.

"Is this true—what I hear of Bobadilla?" demanded Columbus.

"I don't know what you've heard, My Lord," answered one. "He asked us to give you this."

Columbus accepted what he saw at once was a royal letter. He did not fail to notice, with a chill of alarm, that it was addressed to "Don Christopher Columbus, Our Admiral of the Ocean Sea and of all the Islands and Mainland of the Indies," without mention of him as viceroy or governor. The letter was meant, also, for his two brothers, Diego and Bartholomew.

He read it with dismay and anger. It called upon him to recognize Francisco de Bobadilla as the new governor and chief magistrate of Española, and to surrender to him "all forts, houses, ships, arms, munitions—in short, all such things as are the property of the crown. We beg you to believe Bobadilla and to do as he asks."

"I sent for a magistrate," cried Columbus. "Bobadilla is no magistrate."

"He is more, My Lord," said the new governor's representative.

Angered, Columbus made no move to see Bobadilla.

The new governor waited only two weeks. Then, on the fifteenth of September, he sent formal notification to Columbus that he possessed letters appointing him, Bobadilla, governor.

Columbus answered at once to say that he had letters appointing him to that post from the king and queen. He made it plain to Bobadilla that he did not intend to honor the letters Bobadilla had.

Within a few days Columbus awoke one morning to find his rooms surrounded by soldiers sent by Bobadilla.

"What is the meaning of this?" he asked the captain of the guard.

"My Lord, I must place you under arrest."

"I give the orders here, captain."

"No, My Lord—it is now Bobadilla who is governor. We have already arrested Don Diego. I am sorry, My Lord—we can only obey."

Columbus submitted and went with the soldiers to the fortress. There he was put in irons, as Diego had been before him. Though he was deeply troubled, he comforted Diego.

"Do not worry, Diego. We may be in prison now, but we'll go to Castile and the king and queen will put an end to this."

"And Bartholomew?"

"As soon as he reaches Santo Domingo, they'll arrest him, too. They want to be rid of us."

Bartholomew joined them in a few days. He, too, was put in irons which secured his hands and feet.

Day after day Columbus and his brothers waited. Columbus spent most of his waking hours on his knees, praying and asking God what he had done to deserve this humiliation. But in his heart he was sure he knew—God was punishing him for the sin of pride. He had been too anxious for worldly glory; he had thought too little of the other world. He had not properly fulfilled his vows, even

though he had brought priests who were estab-
lishing missions among the natives.

Three weeks passed. Then, on the twelfth of
October—the eighth anniversary of Columbus'
landing at Guanahani—a visitor came. Columbus
recognized him as Alonso de Vallejo, one of the
gentlemen of the settlement.

"Will you come with me to the caravel, My
Lord?" he asked.

"Vallejo, where are you taking me?" demanded
Columbus.

"Sir, Your Lordship is now going to embark."

"Is this true, Vallejo?"

"By Your Lordship's life, you're going to take
ship for Spain." He stood aside for Columbus to
pass. "You are in my charge, My Lord."

As soon as Columbus and his brothers were on
board ship, Vallejo and the caravel master came
to him.

"We've come, My Lord, to take off your
chains," said Vallejo.

But Columbus shook his head. "No. I thank
you. I've been put into fetters by the orders of the
king and queen. None but they can deliver me.
This is God's punishment upon me. Let me wear

the fetters until the king and queen deliver me."

"It shall be as you wish, My Lord," answered Vallejo.

The two men withdrew, leaving Columbus to his fetters and prayers.

Columbus still wore his irons when the ship reached Cadiz late in November. He had not once removed them. He had actually grown proud of them because they were a constant reminder of how sinful his pride had been. He had, nevertheless, written to the king and queen while still on board the *La Gorda*. The captain of the ship saw to it that his letters were sent at once, before Vallejo could bring to the court at Granada the documents from Bobadilla justifying his arrest of the Columbus brothers.

From the ship Columbus and his brothers went to prison on shore.

Within a few days a special courier from the king and queen arrived with orders that they be freed and present themselves at Granada. The king and queen were grieved and deeply shocked to learn that their Admiral of the Ocean Sea had been put into irons and jailed. They had not meant Bobadilla to go so far. They sent two thousand ducats so that the Columbus brothers might appear before their majesties outfitted as was proper for their rank.

Columbus and his brothers reached Granada in the middle of December. They went to court without delay. Though Bartholomew and Diego had obeyed the order of the king and queen to dress according to their station, Columbus wore only the plain brown Franciscan robe with the sleeves thrown back so that all might see the marks of the irons.

Diego stood silent before the king and queen.

Bartholomew likewise stood, but he was not silent. "I was abroad when the discovery of the Indies took place, your majesties. I was called to Castile and assured by my brother that I would be honored. This was confirmed by letters from your majesties. I have given seven years of my life to this quest—and in five of them I have hardly slept in a bed, or been free of death at my side. Now I have been put in irons and my honors have been taken from me. I ask my salary. My services are available to your majesties—but if these are not wanted, I ask my freedom since I am well able to take care of myself."

"We shall do you no injustice, Don Bartholomew," assured King Ferdinand.

Columbus, meanwhile, was aware that every
eye was upon him. He fell to his knees in homage,
and he wept because he was helpless before the
power and might of his sovereigns. The queen was
disturbed by his humility and spoke to him gently.

"Rise, My Lord. Do yourself no injustice. It
grieves us to see these marks upon your wrists."

Columbus rose to his feet and raised his silver-
haired head. His eyes flashed to Queen Isabel, and
from her to the king, and from him to stern-faced
Cardinal Cisneros, who stood near and seemed to
disapprove of him.

"My loyalty to your majesties has never been in
question," he said. "And I willingly confess my
errors. But none was ever made—I say it here before God—none was ever made that was not made
in good faith, for any man might make a mistake."

"But you are not just any man, My Lord Admiral," answered Queen Isabel quietly. "You are
our Admiral of the Ocean Sea. In you we looked
for less of the weakness and bad judgment common to all men. Perhaps it was that we expected

too much of you, My Lord. The glory of your discoveries has not been diminished, though there are
those who tell us that these lands of yours are a new
world and not the Indies. No matter. We shall
restore your honors. But it is our decision that you
are to go no more to Española."

"I am your humble servant, your majesty," answered Columbus.

"Now, My Lord, do compose yourself. Two of
my pages are most anxious to be greeted by you.
We shall make them wait no longer."

Queen Isabel turned and beckoned. Two boys
came forward, one almost a man, the other only
thirteen.

Columbus hardly recognized them as his sons,
Diego and Fernando. They came toward them and
he rushed upon them to embrace them with cries
of proud joy. How well they looked! How cleanly
they were dressed! And what fine manners they
had learned as pages for the queen!

Queen Isabel rose, smiling. The court followed
suit. "We shall excuse you, My Lord, so that you
may be with your sons."

Next day Columbus had another audience with

the king and queen. He talked at great length, explaining his work in Española, but it was clear to him that their majesties did not intend him to go back to the Indies—neither as governor nor as explorer. Queen Isabel suggested that perhaps he might like to attach himself to the court, but this he rejected with thanks. He was a man of action; he was now only forty-nine; he meant to do still more exploring.

From that day forward Columbus planned upon another voyage. He prayed constantly for God's favor. He cast about for something which would soften Cardinal Cisneros' opposition to him. Perhaps he could fulfill the prophecy of Esdras and sail to liberate Jerusalem by finding that Prester John's kingdom of which Messer Marco Polo had written, and there join forces with that Christian country to free the Holy Land.

He wrote to the king and queen, filled with enthusiasm about this project. He quoted the prophecies and gave many cogent reasons why he should be allowed to go on this mission. But he delayed sending his letter, for he learned that other explorers were being granted patents to sail across the western sea. He learned, too, that the Portu-

guese explorers were sailing toward the lands he
had discovered.

For months he sought some way of reaching the
king and queen with a plan that would seize their
imaginations and put him once again in their good
favor. He began to think of what the Italian mapmakers were beginning to say—that he had discovered a new world. Perhaps this was true.
Would it not explain his failure to find the Grand
Khan of Cathay? Would it not explain his inability
to discover Cipango? Perhaps. He was not entirely
convinced. But, he reasoned, if this were so—ac-
cepting the possibility—then surely the Indies lay
beyond in other seas, and there must be a passage
by water—narrow, to be sure—which led beyond
the lands he had discovered to other seas, and, beyond them, to the long-sought Indies.

This was the idea he had looked for. He wrote
in haste to the king and queen and set his plan before them. He timed his letter well, for Francisco
de Bobadilla had just been recalled, and Don Frey
Nicolás de Ovando had been sent to Española as
the new governor. Ovando had sailed with 2,500
men and twelve Franciscan friars. He had also been
instructed to return to the Columbus brothers all

personal property which had been taken by Bobadilla.

Columbus' letter thus came before the king and
queen at the right moment. They did not hesitate
to grant Columbus' request for ships to seek a passage to seas beyond the western sea. They permitted Fernando to leave the court and sail with
him, since Columbus had asked that his younger
son be allowed to go with him on this voyage. And,
once again, Bartholomew stood ready to go.

But Columbus was forbidden to call at Española
on the way out, though he might visit there on the
way back if he wished. He was reminded, too, of
his errors, for the letters patent included these
warnings—"While it is true that your staff must
obey you without question, we adjure you to remember that you must treat them as men in our
service and not as only your personal servants.
They, too, are Spaniards. And, finally, you must
not bring slaves to us."

Columbus was overjoyed just the same. He
granted that he deserved the implied chiding of
the king and queen. He thanked God for answering his prayers and hastened to buy and outfit four
ships. In his arrangements for men to man his ships

he had no trouble, for the fever of exploration now filled all Spain as a result of the discoveries he had made.

The little fleet sailed from Cadiz on the ninth of May, 1502.

12 The Last Voyage

FOR a year Columbus sailed in search of a strait
to lead him to the seas beyond the western sea. He
sought in vain. He sailed first to Santo Domingo,
intending to go east and south from there. But a
hurricane was brewing when he reached Santo Domingo late in June; so he sent ashore asking Governor Ovando for permission to anchor in the
mouth of a river there until the hurricane blew by.
Seeing that a fleet of ships was preparing to leave

the harbor for Spain, Columbus added a warning that the ships should not be permitted to go until after the storm.

Governor Ovando sent back a curt refusal. He scorned Columbus' warning and ordered the fleet to sail. Columbus did not wait to see how the hurricane destroyed and sank nineteen of the ships of that fleet but sailed to a safe harbor in the mouth of a river not far to the west of Santo Domingo. There his fleet rode out the hurricane.

From there, once the hurricane had blown itself out, he sailed southwest, then east, and south. In many places he stopped to barter with the Indians, always adding gold to his stores. In one place he tried to establish a settlement, which, since the day was the sixth of January, he named Belén, after Bethelehem, in honor of the Three Kings. But this, too, failed, and the settlers withdrew and returned to the ships, driven back by the attacks of unfriendly Indians whose weapons, even if they were no match for the Spaniards, killed some of the men.

By May—a year after Columbus had left Spain —he reached the coast of Jamaica. He was ill, feverish, and weary. Only two ships remained to him of the four with which he had started, and neither of these was seaworthy any longer. Columbus tried to reach Española, but he was forced to return to Jamaica, where the ships were run aground on a sand beach near a friendly Indian village.

They were in a bay which Christopher had named Santa Gloria on his second voyage. Columbus knew that they would be here for a long time. He sent a party of men to hunt for food and to make arrangements for the Indians to continue to supply the 116 men aboard the ships with food while they stayed there.

Then he redoubled his efforts in prayer. He felt sure that God's infinite compassion would be visited upon him when he had expiated his sins.

One night, while he lay in troubled sleep, he seemed to hear a gentle voice speak to him alone. "Has not your God always cared for you? Has He not always protected you from the time of your birth? When you were at the proper age did He not make your name resound over the earth? Did He not give you the key to the shackles of the ocean sea? What more did He do for the people of Israel—for David, whom he raised to be king of Judea? Turn your face to Him and know your error. Fear not. Be trustful. All your troubles are written on stone. All are with cause."

He awoke with a start and in the night resolved to do all in his power to speed his voyage. In the morning he called together his officers and sat to plan the repair of the ships. But this could not be done. As all the officers pointed out, they lacked tools and materials. They needed a new ship, and where, but from Governor Ovando in Santo Domingo, could they hope to find one?

The chief notary of the fleet, Diego Méndez, came one day to where Columbus sat talking with his son, Fernando, who had grown strong and tall in the sufferings he had endured on the voyage.

"Sir," said Méndez, "we're in grave danger. I think you know it. These caravels will never sail again. The longer we remain, the more dissatisfied the men will become, and the natives also will grow more scornful of us."

"I know this, Méndez," answered Columbus. "I ask God daily to guide me."

"Sir, it would be difficult—perhaps impossible —for a canoe to go to Española from here. It is forty leagues of water . . ."

"But someone must go to Ovando if we are to be set free."

"Sir, must it be I?" asked Méndez. "I've put my life in danger many times to save yours and the men with us."

"And each time our Lord has spared you," answered Columbus. "Is there better reason for such choice? He will spare you again."

"Sir, ask the men if any will go, which I doubt. When they have all refused, I shall put my life at your service if it be to the death. I've done it before."

One man volunteered to go with Méndez. The two set out one day in July, carrying letters to Governor Ovando and also others to be sent forward to the king and queen. Columbus ordered them to deliver the letter to Governor Ovando in person and then to return to Spain, trusting to Ovando to send them a ship.

The little canoe with the two men in it was soon lost to sight in the vast expanse of the sea.

Then they waited.

The weeks lengthened into months. Summer became autumn, and autumn winter. As the year turned, the events which Méndez had foreseen began to take shape.

First, on the second of January the captain of one of the ships led a revolt against the admiral, though Columbus was so ill he could hardly walk. The rebels seized Columbus' canoes and tried to follow Méndez, but the sea beat them back. They returned to Jamaica, staying apart from Columbus and those who remained faithful to him.

At the same time the Indians became more menacing. Each day seamen told of new mutterings. Columbus knew that something more would have to be done to impress the natives with the strength and wisdom of the white men, for the revolt of the captain and his followers had shown the Indians that there was no unity among them. And the failure of the ships to set sail made them believe that the Spaniards were not so strong as they pretended to be, nor so close to God as they claimed to be when they spoke of Christianity.

Columbus called all the chiefs together by sending word that he wished to speak to them about a matter of great importance. He set the time of the meeting for evening of the twenty-ninth of February. He chose this date because he knew by a

calendar he had with him that there would be a
total eclipse of the moon on that night.

The chiefs came to listen to Columbus, who
stood on the castle aft, weak and ill, but determined. The Indians stood or sat in the tall grass
along the shore beyond the sandy beach. Some
were on the ship itself, together with one of their
number who was the interpreter for what the
white chief would say to them.

Columbus spoke simply, slowly, and with effort.

"I speak to you of the great God above us," he
said, pointing into the heavens. "He is the special
protector of the white man. He wishes me to say
to you that you must continue to trade with us and
to remain peaceful, or He will punish you."

He waited while the interpreter translated this,
paying no attention to the mutterings of protest.

Then he went on. "This very evening our Lord
will send you a sign to say that He is not pleased
with you. He will take the moon from the sky."

The interpreter hesitated, grinned, and prepared
to laugh. But Columbus was solemn. The interpreter repeated what he had said. The moon was
even now rising, plain for all to see. The white
chief did not know of what he spoke. There were

laughs and chuckles; there were also cries of anger.

Columbus was unmoved. He stood watching the hourglass before him, looking from it to the moon. When he saw the shadow begin to form on the edge of the moon, he pointed silently.

The Indians, seeing, began to cry out in fear. They begged him to intercede with God and restore the moon. They promised to remain friendly and to obey the white chief if only God would no longer be displeased with them.

"I will go into my cabin and talk with God," said Columbus.

He went from the castle aft and sat watching the progress of the eclipse, praying that God might permit this ruse to have the desired effect. When the eclipse was almost total, he came out once more and mounted the castle. He held up his hands to still the clamor of the Indians' frightened voices.

"God has said He will restore the moon. Watch upon His goodness."

As the shadow passed from the face of the moon, the natives and their chiefs shouted with joy.

This evidence of the might of the white men quieted the Indians. But the rebels among the Spaniards were not put down until Bartholomew

Columbus took a force of men and captured their leader.

Still there was no word from Governor Ovando. There was no way of knowing whether Diego Méndez had completed his journey safely. Winter grew to spring, and spring to summer. And then, a year after Méndez had set out on the dangerous voyage, two ships came from Governor Ovando.

Méndez had reached Santo Domingo safely, but the governor had hesitated to dispatch the ships Columbus wanted until the people and the priests had begun to criticize him openly. Only then, reluctantly, had he sent them. Columbus immediately wrote the governor a letter of thanks and set sail from Jamaica for Santo Domingo, and from there, on September 12, 1504, for Spain.

On the seventh of November Columbus reached Sanlúcar de Barrameda, where the Guadalquivir River enters the sea. He wrote at once to the king and queen, and he wrote, too, to his son, Diego. He hoped to be asked to call upon his sovereigns, but no letter came. From his son came word only that Queen Isabel was gravely ill. This explained his lack of an invitation to court, Columbus told himself.

At the same time he had not been home long before the yearning to set sail again took hold of him. All that month he fretted. Then, early in December, he learned that Isabel the Catholic had died on the twenty-sixth of November.

He was grieved to learn of her death for two reasons, apart from her kindness toward him. Now he would have to wait longer than ever to see King Ferdinand—at least until the period of mourning was past. And now he had less hope than before that his power and privileges, taken from him after Bobadilla had become governor of Española, would be restored to him.

Nevertheless, ill as he himself was, he wrote constantly to all his friends at court. He did not forget that his son, Diego, was still close to the king. He wrote advising him to consult with Archbishop Deza of Seville—that same Deza who had been responsible for his first voyage— about matters which concerned Columbus. Shrewdly he sent his second son, Fernando, back to the court to be with his brother, to whom he could speak of his adventures on his voyage and of the lands he had seen—all of which would reach the court.

The king wrote at last to say that he would be happy to listen to his Admiral of the Ocean Sea.

In May Columbus left Seville and went to Segovia, where the king waited to see him.

King Ferdinand was friendly. He looked a little tired, as if his grief for the queen had not yet been tempered. He listened with great care and attention while Columbus spoke and answered him fairly.

"It seems to us, My Lord, that you are too ill to make another voyage," he said in response to Columbus' suggestion. "And as for your affairs— these claims you press for your privileges and money—surely it would be best, would it not, if someone were in charge of them so that we may, for our part, settle them?"

"Let it be anyone your majesty orders," answered Columbus.

"Who, then?" asked the king.

"Could anyone be better than Archbishop Deza? He, more than anyone else, except your royal chamberlain, is responsible for your majesty now ruling these lands I found."

"It shall be done."

Columbus was disappointed that the king had not looked kindly upon his plan to go on another voyage. His disappointment aggravated his illness and he took to his bed, from which he wrote to Archbishop Deza in despair, saying, "Perhaps I am wrong in fighting for my privileges. I am an old man, not long for this world, and this battle is like whipping the winds. It would be best that I should let God, our Lord, decide these things, for I have ever found Him propitious. I fear I have put more diligence into serving the king and queen than in reaching for paradise. This loss of my privileges should be but one punishment."

Though he continued to dream of making another voyage, his health did not return. Wherever he went, he spent most of his time lying ill in bed, waiting in vain for any authority from King Ferdinand to go to sea again, or for any restoration of his privileges for himself and for his heirs. Despite all that his sons could do at court, the king was silent. And Columbus grew steadily weaker.

It was now 1506. Columbus had been home in Valladolid a year and a half, and he had made no progress toward renewed health. Nor had he achieved any goal at court. Letters to the king and the archbishop, representations to Cardinal Cisneros, prayers and penance—none availed him.

As spring wore on, Columbus' illness grew worse. One day in May the doctor who attended him suggested that he ought to make his will. Columbus sent at once for the notary and, when he came, issued orders about what to set down.

"My heir," he said, "shall be my son Diego. So write this for me to sign. Fernando shall have his equal part. I wish Diego to keep a chapel, and I desire that in it three priests shall say three Masses a day—one in honor of the Holy Trinity, one of the conception of Our Lady, one for the souls of my father, mother, and wife. Say to Diego to watch over the welfare of Fernando's mother as he would have of his own."

He gave many more instructions. The notary copied all he said and placed the document before him to sign. Columbus signed it with a trembling, uncertain hand.

This was on the nineteenth of May. After it was done, the doctor comforted him. "You may live longer than I think, My Lord. Take heart. They are saying, My Lord—throughout all Spain—that you have found a new world."

"A westward passage by water to the Indies," said Columbus. "Is that a new world? But what have I to live for on this earth? I have found new lands for God and king, as I vowed to do, and others have already gone to spread God's word among them."

Next day was the feast of the Ascension. Columbus was no better. Méndez came to see him, and a priest came to give him the last sacraments and say a Mass. Columbus, his friends, and the servants who attended him, received Holy Communion.

Columbus murmured, "My spirit is now in God's hands."

Having said this, Columbus spoke no more. He was resigned to God's will. For the last time he turned from the western sea and the lands he had found—turned from the glory and the power which had made him Admiral of the Ocean Sea—and made his lonely voyage to God.

VISION BOOKS